P9-CCU-531

THE BIBLE AND THE ORIGIN OF MAN

The BIBLE *and the* ORIGIN *of* MAN

JEAN DE FRAINE, S. J.
(Doctor of Biblical Sciences)

DIVISION OF THE SOCIETY OF ST. PAUL
STATEN ISLAND, N. Y. 10314

The Bible and the Origin of Man is a translation from the revised Dutch edition *De Bijbel en het Ontstaan van de Mens* first published in Antwerp, Belgium, by S. A. Sheed & Ward in 1956.

De licentia Superiorum Ordinis.

NIHIL OBSTAT
Myles M. Bourke, S.S.L., S.T.D.

IMPRIMATUR
✠ Francis Cardinal Spellman
Archbishop of New York
December 6, 1961

The nihil obstat and imprimatur are official declarations that a book or pamphlet is free of doctrinal or moral error. No implication is contained therein that those who have granted the nihil obstat and imprimatur agree with the contents, opinions or statements expressed.

1st Edition, 1962 2nd Edition, 1967
Library of Congress Catalog Card Number: 67 - 15497

Printed and bound in the U.S.A. by the Pauline Fathers and Brothers as part of their communications apostolate.

Contents

Biblical quotations are from the Confraternity of Christian Doctrine edition, except where otherwise indicated.

Introduction

> *"The question of questions for mankind—the problem which underlies all others, and is more deeply interesting than any other—is the ascertainment of the place which Man occupies in nature and of his relations to the universe of things."* [1]

THESE WORDS of Th. H. Huxley express the guiding idea of modern anthropology. The discovery of fossil man, from the Gibraltar skull (1848) to *Zinjanthropus* (August 1959) has steadily put back the date of the first appearance of man. Besides, the theory of evolution is more and more applied to the human organism as well, though with increasing awareness of the

[1] Th. H. Huxley, *Man's Place in Nature*, New York, 1899. p. 76

complexity of the problems. The hypothesis of a direct evolution from a well-determined group of primates has been resolutely turned down. Science is more and more preoccupied with the problem of monogenesis. The difficulties in this area have been considerably increased by the simultaneous presence of *Homo Neanderthalensis* and of *Homo Sapiens*, and especially by the more recent discoveries in South Africa. It is believed that an intermediate species between primate and man has been found there, called the *Australopithecinae*.

In the presence of these scientific data a conscientious Catholic cannot help wondering: "What relation is there between these scientific findings and the teachings of faith contained in the inspired books?"

Such a question did not even arise a century ago. Nothing cast the slightest doubt on the certitude of biblical teaching. For the majority of Christians no problem arose about the age of humanity, the origin of man, or the unity of mankind. The reason for that was very simple. The biblical texts were interpreted quite literally. The exact date of creation could be calculated; the first man had been directly created by God (perhaps formed from clay); the names of Adam and Eve made it evident enough that only one couple had reached the human estate.

There can be no doubt that these ancient and rather naive conceptions are in conflict with the data of scientific prehistory. And quite a number of people are disturbed about this conflict. Intellectuals are sometimes inclined to agree with rationalistic Scripture interpretation which, in the name of "science," relegates the biblical narrative to the realm of mythical imagination. Such a position, however, is based on an inadmissible rejection of one of the terms of a paradox. The latter can no doubt be solved in another way. Only a sound interpretation of scientific data and of the teachings of Holy Scripture will allow us to solve the problem of the origin of man correctly. It is only an unprejudiced attitude, which takes both elements of the problem into account, that will do justice to the ideal of Catholic truthfulness.

The aim of this book[2] is to realize as exactly as possible the real meaning of the main biblical texts on this subject. Three chapters set forth this explanation. The first describes the paradox mentioned above, and outlines the wide range of the solution. The second studies in detail the principal biblical texts which relate to the origin of man. Finally a third chapter compares these biblical interpretations with the teachings of the Church. For all Catholic exegesis must take into consideration authentic doctrine as it is set forth by the supernatural Catholic community. However, this doctrine may be considered from a triple point of view. First of all, man's origin presents some aspects indissolubly linked with certain solemnly defined dogmas. Next, we must take into account certain declarations of the ordinary teaching of the Church. Finally, the Church is more particularly interested in the origin of man in some very precise

[2] The work constitutes the author's revised interpretation of a study in Dutch in the collection "Logos" (1953).

documents. All these statements of Church authorities, with their various degrees of importance, must guide the judgment of the faithful Catholic. The Bible as a source of faith, as the inspired Word of God exempt from error, must indeed be interpreted in the bosom of the Church.

It follows that the strictly exegetical job of trying to determine the exact doctrinal meaning of the biblical texts, even with their original inspiration, deserves attention and will prove to be particularly enlightening. The present study has no other purpose but to face this problem. In concentrating so much on scriptural data, it practically leaves aside the teachings of dogmatic Tradition, that no less authoritative source of the Catholic faith. The intent of our work is not to show how far one *must* go when presenting Catholic doctrine about man's origin, but rather how far one *may* go without being unfaithful to the biblical expression of that doctrine. We hope that this book may shed some light on these difficult problems in behalf of divine and human truth, which can never really contradict one another.

J.D.F.

Louvain, September 30th, 1959
on the Feast of St. Jerome

THE BIBLE AND THE ORIGIN OF MAN

I *The Problem*

THE ORIGIN OF MAN poses a certain number of problems which, though related, must nevertheless not be confused. First we may inquire whether or not the human organism descends from *preexisting beings in the animal order*, and if so, how; this is the object of research in biological evolution. Next we may ask *at what moment* (doubtless with all possible nuances) the genesis of man took place; the answer devolves upon paleontological anthropology. Finally there is the problem of the *number* of individuals who were first raised to the dignity of the human person. This last problem is, scientifically speaking, very difficult to solve and has for science only a secondary interest.

These three related, but not identical, problems may be

considered from a scientific or from a philosophical point of view. Philosophy plays an important role here. Considerations which may seem secondary to the scientist are of the greatest moment for the philosopher. A scientist, for example, may admit that the great majority of anthropologists accept monophyletism, which is the hypothesis that claims the whole of mankind derives from one single animal stem.[1] The available data of paleontology do not allow the scientist to proceed any further; in particular he cannot decide scientifically between one single original couple (strict monogenesis) or several individuals. But while the scientist considers that question rather unimportant,[2] yet it is of the utmost importance to the philosopher. However the latter must not let himself be led by rationalistic prejudices, but he must keep an open mind for the whole reality. The idea which is formed of people is totally different according to whether the genesis of man is described as the emergence of a spiritual person, or as the formation of a being which, after all, is hardly raised above the animal level. Furthermore, in connection with the evolution of the human body, only the unbiased philosophical idea of a Personal God and Creator can account for the special intervention of that God in the creative act. A personal and free Supreme Being is necessary to determine the numerical importance, the time and the place of the first

[1] E. Boné, S. J., "L'homme, genèse et cheminement," in *Nouvelle Revue Théologique*, 69, (1947), 360-389, p. 381.
[2] H. Weinert, *L'homme préhistorique*, Paris, 1944, p. 48. See also V. Marcozzi, "Poligenesi ed evoluzione nella Origine dell'Uomo," in *Gregorianum*, 29 (1948), p. 362.

"explosive modification" of the original cell (as mutation is generally represented nowadays).

Hence our three problems (the evolution of man, the age of humanity and the number of first "men") may be considered from a scientific and from a philosophical standpoint. To overlook either point of view would lead to an incomplete solution. We could not speak in any way of a "human" problem if we rejected either one of these study methods. All true synthesis ready to accept total reality *must* reconcile the two points of view: since truth is one, apparent conflicts must be resolved and harmonized.

There remains a third method, which consists in investigating the religious meaning of the origin of man. This way of looking at it tries to show that man's beginning is tied in with the fundamental religious concept which unites man with God. This method proves to be perfectly legitimate, indeed even necessary, when it is a question of working out a complete and truly human solution of the problem. The authentic teachings of the Bible are irreplaceable, especially for a Catholic who believes that the Sacred Books have been inspired and cannot be in error in what they really *affirm*. Unquestionably they must be used if we wish to know the complete truth about the origin of man.

Therefore there arises the question: "What relation is there between the biblical texts on the creation of man and the conclusions proved by science?"

To answer this question, it is important above all to follow the wise advice from "The Imitation of Christ":

"All Holy Scripture should be read in the spirit in which it was written."[3] Now it is evident that the authors of the Bible never dreamed of teaching us about scientific prehistory. Therefore we do them an injustice when we evaluate their writings in the light of modern science. They simply never had the intention of dealing with science. What Gregory of Nyssa says about history applies even more to the Genesis account of the creation of man: "When Holy Writ uses historical narrations its purpose is not just to make known the events of the past and what the Ancients have accomplished or suffered, but to give us a rule of life conforming to the precepts of virtue. Therefore the historical narration of facts is directed toward a wider purpose. Everybody agrees that Holy Scripture should be understood in that way."[4]

Whoever looks for anything but the religious meaning of primitive history runs the danger of adopting the slightly ridiculous attitude of a certain number of radio listeners in 1946. In broadcasting a radio sketch it was assumed, in the script, that scientists had lost control of nuclear energy. A few inattentive listeners took for objective news something which was only a dramatic radio play. A severe panic ensued, which spread like wildfire. This misunderstanding was not the fault of the broadcasters, but of the listeners, who had "misunderstood."

[3] Thomas a Kempis, *The Imitation of Christ*, Bk. I, ch. 5.
[4] Greg. Nyssen, *In psalmos*, II, 2, (Greek Patrology of Migne, 44/490).

Something similar can happen in the interpretation of the biblical texts written with a religious purpose. It is an article of faith (although not solemnly defined), that the Bible is free of all error. Yet, when we realize the difference which exists between biblical reports and scientific opinions, we must admit frankly that the absence of harmony is very clear. Before this undeniable fact, two positions are possible. Either we may try to harmonize the concepts of the Bible with scientific discoveries, or we may fully accept the divergence between the religious way of thinking and the scientific way of thinking, between the primitive Semitic mentality and the rationalistic Western mentality.

The first horn of this dilemma leads to truly untenable propositions, and must definitely be rejected. This tendency toward conciliation has received the name of "Concordism." Since 1870 three kinds of Concordism have arisen: astronomical Concordism (for instance, Abbé Moreux's "nebulae" before the stars), geological Concordism (the six days representing six "ages"), and zoological Concordism. But even before the end of the 19th century Concordism was forcefully attacked. Again, efforts have been made to build up some kind of ethnographic Concordism, which claims that the stories of Genesis reflect the economic system of primitive man. But these efforts too have led to failure.

Although most Catholic authors have repudiated Concordism under its many forms, there are still, in our own day, a few scholars who defend some sort of neo-Concordism. In an article published in 1946, the director of the Astronomical Observatory of Rome, G. Armellini, claims that complete harmony exists between the biblical cosmogony and the data of science.[5] For example, the late creation of man (on the sixth day) corresponds to the scientific fact that man did not appear until the Quaternary period.

Such an attitude no longer "understands" the ancient texts; therefore it is severely criticized by most modern exegetes. To quote only one example, here is what D. Buzy says: "Nothing is so contrary to science and especially to sacred science as to subject it principally to conclusions preestablished by some other discipline. For a century, we have tolerated too many of the excesses and naivetés of these à priori comparisons, so that today we want to guard against them, and to restore to exegesis the independence and liberty which should never have been abdicated." [6]

If then, we must reject the first horn of our dilemma, we must necessarily admit the second. If we take into consideration their different ways of thinking, we shall not try to reconcile the Bible and science.[7] It does not follow however that Holy Scripture contains any errors. For an error supposes two conditions:

1. There must be an absolute affirmation. It does not suffice to deal with an opinion which is not verified

[5] G. Armellini, "Cosmogonia moderna e cosmogonia mosaica," in *Studium*, 42 (1946), pp. 152-156.

[6] D. Buzy, "Le Concordisme préhistorique ou la fin du Concordisme" in *Mélanges Podechard*, Lyons, 1945, 17-26, p. 23.

[7] D. Buzy, l.c., 25: "The appearance of biblical man does not coincide with that of prehistoric man; we must disavow a discovery from which indispensable elements are missing."

by the author, or with a widespread unconfirmed concept. It is therefore unfair to accuse the sacred author of error, as long as he has not laid down an explicit affirmation.

2. It must then be a question of an assertion which, in a given medium, corresponds solidly with the author's intention. Now the Bible has been written for simple people, and does not intend to teach us anything about scientific prehistory. What St. Augustine says about inanimate nature applies also to some extent to the detailed description of the origin of man: "God did not intend to teach men about the inner structure of nature, because that could in no way help them to attain their eternal salvation." [8] From this statement of the holy Doctor it follows that there was nothing in the intention of the sacred authors, nor was it God's intention, to satisfy directly our scientific or even our merely human curiosity. God, the principal author of Holy Scripture, intends only one purpose: religious instruction. On the other hand, the human contribution of the sacred author excludes any kind of scientific claims. It serves only as a framework for divine eternal truth. This does not imply that the historical facts contained in this human framework are not an integral part of the inspired texts, nor even that they are not actually affirmed: but they are inspired and affirmed only inasmuch as they

[8] August., *De Genesi ad litteram,* II, 9, 20, in the Latin Patrology of Migne, 34-270. Cf. D. Buzy, l.c., p. 25. "The sacred author speaks of these things, not as a learned man or as a proud scientific writer, but as a man of his time, speaking to his contemporaries in a language which they can understand."

serve the expression of God's thought. Whenever we find "errors" in the Bible, it is always because we make the Bible say things which it does not intend to say, or because we misunderstand what it intends to say. Only the authentic content of the Bible is free from error.

NB

Why do we claim to discover errors in Holy Scripture? Because of our Western, Greco-Roman mentality which impels us to reduce all natural (even supernatural) truth to some scientific system. We consider this "truth" as a part of a vast and complex network of scientific data. But the authors of the Bible were Orientals. Semites, like all Orientals, are never abstract, but always concrete and empirical; the pursuit of a coldly objective, precise science is strange to them. The inspired authors have written their works with a mentality which differs considerably from ours. Therefore we can speak neither of a definite contradiction nor of a positive agreement between the religious conceptions about the origin of man and the authentic facts of science. These last are always the result of a scientific technique or method based on strict and abstract logic. The Bible, on the contrary, teaches us the values, or rather the facts, which refer to salvation. Whether essentially religious and supernatural, or, when purely natural, these values or facts are indispensable as the safeguard of verities and facts in the strictly religious order.[9]

[9] That is why the task of the Catholic exegete is very clearly defined by D. Buzy, l.c., 26: "Free from the worry of 'apologetics' which up to now brought him more disappointments than benefits, he will apply himself more to the study of revealed truths which are offered to him under the pleasing *appearance* of an Oriental literary style."

The Bible is the book of divine condescension. God takes into consideration the mass of men for whom His book is destined. That is why He presents His Word in a language which is adapted equally to the humble and to the simple. It takes a certain simplicity of mind not to consider Holy Scripture as an exact and precise scientific treatise, which it was never intended to be. After all, everything comes down to the words of Christ: "Amen I say to you, whoever does not accept the Kingdom of God as a little child, will not enter into it" (Mk 10:15). Even an adult must definitely continue to read the Bible with the simplicity of a child, and not with the ruthless criticism of the scientist.

It follows from these considerations that our topic, "The Bible and the Origin of Man," must from the start drop more than one false problem. It is certainly true that the material object of scientific prehistory, of the philosophy of man, and of the inspired word of God do partially coincide. These three categories of thought obviously are concerned with the complex but identical reality of man. But the *formal object* of the three methods of investigation shows essential differences. First, science considers man as a living organism, showing a physical descent from other animal species of a somewhat similar nature. Philosophy, on the contrary, emphasizes the spiritual personality of man and the evidences of a personal intervention by the Creator. More thoroughly even than philosophy, the Bible finally probes the essential structure of "homo religiosus," of man who, in the beginning, was created by God, and who continues to be irresistibly drawn by "Deus fascinans."

We never should lose sight of this formal object of the biblical teachings about the origin of man. But it is vain to draw from the Bible information which comes under the formal object of the other disciplines.[10]

For at least two of the problems which were mentioned above, we should not even look for a solution in the Bible.

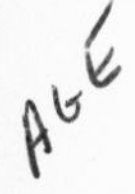

The first of these problems concerns the age of mankind. Science tells us that this age amounts to at least 50,000 years.[11] Now the figures in the Bible do not go beyond 4141 B.C. in the Hebrew original, 5225 B.C. in the Septuagint, and 4200 in the Samaritan version of the Pentateuch. For the time which elapsed between Adam and Abraham, the biblical chronology is based on two genealogical lists, whose figures differ in the three versions. These lists refer to the ten generations between Adam and Noe (Gn 5) and to the ten others connecting Noe to Abraham (Gn 11:10-26). The time between Abraham and Christ is calculated from a few chronological data scattered in subsequent scriptural books. The starting point is the building of the first temple by Solomon, which must be dated about 968 B.C.,

[10] D. Buzy, l.c., 20, notes rightly: "The two stories of the creation (Gn 1-2) and of the fall (Gn 2-3) contain no allusion whatever to a prehistoric period: they take place (according to the report) outside of time and history."

[11] The geologists (v.g. Obermeier, Koeppel, Termier) seem to favor the lowest figures. The anthropologists raise them considerably; among Catholic anthropologists, v.g., E. Boné (l.c. p. 361) speaks of some "500,000 years."

in the fourth year of Solomon's reign. But 3 Kgs 6:1 puts the time which elapsed between the exodus from Egypt and the building of the temple at 480 years. Ex 12:40 tells us that the stay in Egypt lasted 430 years. According to Gn 47:28, Jacob was 130 years old when he went to Egypt; Gn 25:26 tells us that Isaac was 60 years old when he begot Jacob; and finally Gn 21:5 says that Abraham was 100 years old when he became the father of Isaac.

The diversity between the several versions of these genealogies seems to imply that the ancient Hebrews did not believe in the exact numerical value of these figures. Most Bible scholars agree that the Greek translators of the third century before Christ have modified the figures of the original text. The Samaritan version too seems to have introduced some changes: in fact three patriarchs, Jared, Mathusale and Lamech are made to die in the same year, namely the year of the flood. Furthermore we know from the Fathers of the Church, among others from the writings of St. Jerome, that the actual terms of these figures were not always identical in all manuscripts.[12] Could we not assume, in the light of these data, that in the course of the centuries, some modifications may have crept into even the original inspired text? When we closely examine these genealogies, we are struck by their rather artificial form which seems to indicate a premeditated system. In the two genealogies the typical figure of 10 certainly attracts attention: this

[12] St. Jerome, *Liber hebraicarum quaestionum in Genesim*, ch. XXXVIII, in PL. 23/996.

series of ten occurs also in the genealogies of other peoples.[13] All these peculiarities lead up to the following question: Can we be sure that the ancient authors and the writer of Genesis had a strictly numerical reality in mind? And do we correctly "understand" their intentions when we interpret these mathematical details in a literal sense?

Without endorsing the drastic solution of Holzinger, who considers these figures simply as a literary game, many a Catholic exegete of today is inclined to admit an artificial system in these genealogies.[14] It is hardly probable that the "priestly" editors of the Bible texts have inserted totally fictitious *names* in these genealogies, but they certainly took great liberties with the *numbers* used in them. The symbolism of figures has always had a great appeal to Semitic thinking and especially to biblical thinking.[15] The doctrine of the numerical value of the letters of the alphabet, known as "gematry," has been much in vogue in the Ancient Near East. Very likely the significance of the genealogies has nothing to do with mathematical precision. Frequently their meaning is more juridical than chronological: attention is directed not so much to physical generation (and hence

[13] For the first ten kings in Mesopotamia, cf. J. DeFraine, in *Verbum Domini*, 25 (1947), p. 43ff.

[14] Likewise, for example, the 3 times 14 generations from Abraham to Christ in the Gospel of St. Matthew (Mt 1:1-17). The evangelist tends to present Jesus as "three times David" (the numerical value of the Hebrew letters of the name "David" is 14), that is, as the real Messiah; cf. E. B. Allo, O.P., *Evangile et Evangelistes*, Paris, 1944, p. 87.

[15] Cf. the German work of A. Heller, *Biblische Zahlensymbolik*, Stuttgart, 1951, 2d ed.

to chronology) as to the accurate transmission of rights and obligations, even of states of guilt.

On all these grounds, the conclusion is obvious: the genealogies of Gn 5 and 11 tell us nothing about the real age of mankind. Their intention is not to transmit quantitative data, but rather to show how the promises of God, received by Adam and Noe, have been transmitted to the Hebrew people descended from Abraham.

Beside the genealogies there are other chronological indications in the Bible concerning the time which elapsed between Abraham and Christ. There too we perceive the schematic nature of these data. It is evident that the figures about Abraham, Isaac and Jacob must be judged within the framework of the genealogies; it seems impossible to attribute to them a strictly numerical sense. The number of 480 years for the time between the Exodus and the construction of the Temple is manifestly artificial: it includes 12 generations, each generation counting exactly 40 years. The time of the stay in Egypt (430 years) no longer presents a strictly numerical character: the Greek text (and also the Samaritan text) includes in this period the time of the residence of the Patriarchs in Canaan.

It is clear then: according to Holy Scripture itself, these data, which at first sight seem to be strictly chronological, can hardly be interpreted as being of a numerical order. Therefore a conscientious commentator has the right and the duty to abstain completely from every effort to derive from the Bible any opinion about the age of mankind.

It is likewise a mistake to try to find in the Bible the unique solution of the biological problem of *evolution.* Of course, when some proponents of the theory of evolution leave the domain of scientific observation and induction to indulge improperly in philosophical speculations, they commit a fault of method. They thus clash with the philosophical and universally human foundation of the religious teachings of the Bible. By virtue of these very considerations, they can be refuted. It is evident that monistic evolutionism is inadmissible, because it is based upon a philosophy which excludes *à priori* a personal God. On the other hand, the Bible emphasizes, as an elementary principle, not only God's immanence, but also His transcendence and His personal character. Since this is a condition preliminary to all religious and personal contact with God, it is evident that monistic evolutionism is incompatible with the teachings of the Bible.

But when the proponents of the theory of evolution accept the philosophical data about the spiritual soul and about God's personal causality in the world, it is clear that the Bible is not at all opposed to the hypothesis of the human body developing, by natural evolution, from non-human organisms. The special intervention of God, required by the biblical texts, is sufficiently taken care of by the creation and infusion of the soul, by which an organism becomes "human." The Bible does not say that this intervention of God should derogate in any way from the ordinary laws of Divine Providence. God might very well have made use of some previously formed animated matter; His special intervention would have consisted in this, that by His own personal choice He would have prepared this animated organic matter for the reception of a human soul. The objection taken from the biblical account of the origin of Eve, and the alleged creation of Adam as an adult, misinterpret the meaning of that account, or at least the intentions of its authors, as will be shown in the second part of this work.

As for the third problem, that of monogenesis, here too one might wonder whether the Bible solves it with sufficient clarity. For to be able to speak of a genuine solution, the sacred author must have intended to consider the problem as such. Do the texts of Genesis, for example, clearly and distinctly teach "theological monogenesis," which says that "all true men, present and past, have descended from a single ancestor"? This question, like many others, can be solved only through an objective study of the texts.

II *The Main Passages of the Bible*

CHRIST HAS ENTRUSTED to the Church the task of the authentic interpretation of Holy Scripture and the protection of the deposit of revealed truths. The harmonious unity of dogmas constitutes what has been called the "analogia fidei," the positive norm to which the Catholic exegete must conform.

It is important then, to examine the main Bible texts on the origin of man within the framework of Catholic doctrine. This will be presented in some detail in the following chapter. In the present chapter we would like to examine the meaning of the five texts which are generally quoted in connection with our topic, namely, Genesis 1:26-28; Genesis 2:7; Genesis 2:18-24; Romans 5:12-19 and Acts 17:26.

It is clear that during this inquiry the ancient texts must be understood in their literal sense, that is, as meaning that which the sacred authors intended them to mean. It is this literal meaning which must be scrutinized first of all, out of reverence for the inspired text itself. The supernatural character of Holy Scripture consists precisely in this, that whatever the *sacred author* affirms as his religious conviction, or as his inspired and therefore infallible testimony, is also affirmed by the Spirit of God. If, then, we want to become acquainted with God's teaching about the origin of man, our first task is to come into contact with the sacred author's religious ideas and testimony, and to carefully weigh the assertions which he expresses. Doubtless it is in a *theological* perspective that there takes place a comparison of the different texts with each other. For a total synthesis of the faith, it is also necessary to consult Tradition. Yet the basic task remains to search for the scriptural meaning directly inspired by God. Moreover, this research must be the most extensive possible, in order to reach the whole objective truth contained in the texts.[1]

[1] Cf. the Encyclical, "Divino afflante Spiritu," 1943.

1. Genesis 1:26–28

God said, "Let us make mankind in our image and likeness; and let them have dominion over the fish of the sea, the birds of the air, the cattle, over all the wild animals and every creature that crawls on the earth." God created man in his image. In the image of God he created him. Male and female he created them. Then God blessed them and said to them, "Be fruitful and multiply; fill the earth and subdue it. Have dominion over the fish of the sea, the birds of the air, the cattle and all the animals that crawl on the earth."

This text clearly pictures the special care with which God surrounded the creation of man. In the artificial setting of the grandiose narrative of creation, which is relayed in the first chapter of the Bible, the origin of man constitutes the culminating point. After having recalled, as a matter of record, the great dogmatic fact: "In the beginning God created the heavens and the earth," [2] the sacred author uses the ideas of his time concerning the "universe" in order to describe what is contained therein. First he points out with an abundance of images the desolation of the starting point: the earth, a flat disc, is covered on its whole surface with water; opaque "darkness" is gathered over it; a tempestuous wind blows violently. From this desolate beginning God proceeds to

[2] Gn 1:1. This proposition means: the first thing which we can state about God, His first manifestation outside of His own nature, is the wonderful, new work of creation, that is, the production of a universe of beings distinct from Himself.

create "all things." In the first three stipulated "days," the boundaries of three divisions within the universe are fixed: the sky (light separated from darkness, Gn 1:3-5), the air (the waters above the firmament separated from the waters beneath it, Gn 1:6-8), and the surface of the earth (the seas separated from the land, and the vegetation thereon, Gn 1:9-13). During the three following "days" God must fill these three regions thus prepared. The sky is filled through the creation of heavenly bodies (Gn 1:14-19), the air is filled with birds (Gn 1:20-23), and the surface of the earth receives the fishes of the sea and the beasts of the land (Gn 1:20-25). At the end of creation, that is, not necessarily last in time,[3] but rather as a conclusion of the narrative, man makes his appearance.

The creation of man is introduced by a very solemn formula. The plural, "let *us* make mankind," should not be interpreted as a remnant of polytheism, as if for instance, this were concerned with the "council of the gods" as is the case in the parallel Babylonian texts. For the following verse speaks of man as made in "the image of God": the pronoun-suffix "his" is manifestly in the singular. Furthermore it would be very strange if the author of the account had maintained a really polytheistic formula, which would be diametrically opposed to his undeniable monotheism. Other commentators, for instance Philo of Alexandria, a Jewish author of the first century after Christ, have seen in this formula

[3] Therefore there is no contradiction here with Gn 2:7, where the creation of man is stated as being in the first place.

an allusion to God's heavenly court, the angels, who are mentioned in the beginning of the book of Job. This interpretation too must be rejected: nowhere in Holy Scripture is the activity of the angels identified with that of God, and it has never been said that man was created in the image of the angels. Certain Fathers of the Church, St. Irenaeus, St. Hilary or St. Basil, detected in this text an indication of the Most Holy Trinity; but such a significance, at least in its complete clarity,[4] seems not very probable in an author of the Old Testament. It is much more preferable to interpret the formula as a plural of majesty, or better yet, as a "plural of exhortation," by which God, as it were, prompts Himself to produce a "new" work and rejoices in it beforehand. At any rate, the terms have a great solemnity; undoubtedly the sacred author wanted to emphasize here a very deliberate plan of God at the time of the creation of man.

What does the term "mankind" mean in this context? The Hebrew *'âdâm* has certainly a collective meaning, as is evident from the plural of the original text and of the Greek Septuagint version, "let *them* have dominion" (literally: "victoriously trample on"). Did

[4] P. Denis, O.P., *Les origines du monde et de l'humanité*, (Liège, 1950) p. 110, mentions the hypothesis defended by Fr. Lagrange, in an article of *Revue Biblique*, 3 (1896), p. 387. "If (God) uses the plural, it implies that there is within Himself such a fullness that He can deliberate with Himself, as several people deliberate among themselves. The Mystery of the Trinity is not definitely indicated, but it gives the best explanation of this term yet to be presented." Does every deliberation necessarily suppose several people? Even individual people sometimes use the plural: "Now, let us see." Cf. also E. F. Sutcliffe, *A Catholic Commentary on Holy Scripture*, London, 1951, p. 102.

the ancient author have in mind only two individuals? It is certain that, in the hymn of jubilation which we find in Gn 1:27, before there is any mention of the sexes, man is considered in general, namely in his relation to his Creator. After that reference, the object of God's creative activity passes from the singular to the plural: "male and female he created *them*."[5] Two attitudes are possible here, according to whether the accent is put on one or another point of view. If we consider the opposition: "God—created human being," we may apply the plural "he created *them*" to the human community in which both sexes are represented equally; if we assume that the plural refers, in the author's opinion, to two, and only two, individuals, the plural form is explained also in that way.[6] At any rate, the narration emphasizes the "species" rather than the number of first men. Undoubtedly in the author's mind the question has not explicitly come up, because he admitted spontaneously that only two individuals had been created by God. But his attention was not much focused on this spontaneous belief; indeed in the following verse his glance goes toward the whole *earth*, which man must *fill* and *subdue*. Here he has undoubtedly given up the individualistic point of view, to give place to a com-

[5] The same terms are used in Gn 5:1-2: "When God created man, he made *him* in the likeness of God. Male and female he created *them* . . . and called *them* Man when they were created." Cf. J. Pedersen, *Israel. Its Life and Culture*, London-Copenhagen, 1946, 2d ed., I-II, 61.

[6] Cf. C. Hauret, *Origine de l'univers et de l'homme d'apres la Bible*, Luçon, 1950, p. 84. "The animals appeared 'according to their kind.' On the subject of Man the narrator changes his formula and insists on the distinction between the sexes: 'male and female he created them.'"

prehensive general view; in the text he is not concerned with an individual as such, but with "eternal man." Therefore it seems to us that this text alone does not teach us anything positive about the problem of monogenesis, for the simple reason that the author is not explicitly and directly interested in that problem, and does not infallibly "affirm" any solution.[7]

What, then, is affirmed in this text? The religious and ethical fact that the very first beings who deserve the name of "man" are entirely dependent upon the Creator. Up to three times they are mentioned as the object of His creative activity. Moreover this dependence forms the basis of a truly voluntary attachment: man finds in himself an "image and likeness" of God Himself.

How shall we interpret the term image? The original text does not use the conjunction *and* between "image" and "likeness." The Fathers of the Church have often made a distinction: man would be an "image" in his nature and a "likeness" through a supernatural gift. But this explanation does not derive from the text as such. The Hebraic terms mean on the one hand an "external representation" (often a devotional image;[8] sometimes a "shadow"), and on the other hand, a "likeness." When both words are united (without the conjunction), their best translation is: "according to a more or less similar representation." This formula contains *in a nut-*

[7] Cf. J. Renié, S.M., *Les origines de l'humanité*, Paris, 1950, p. 102. "We can . . . admit that the first story of creation contained in Genesis can, if necessary, agree with the polygenetic hypothesis."

[8] Cf. T. Maertens, O.S.B., *Les sept jours (Genèse 1)*, Bruges, 1951, pp. 57-58.

shell the full religious meaning of the analogy of being. Man is an image of God, yet he remains always at a distance from Him who is Perfect and totally Other.

We wonder what the fact of being an image of God amounts to concretely. A few authors explain Gn 1:27 by Gn 5:3, where it is said that "when Adam was 130 years old, he became the father of a son in his own likeness, after his image, and he called him Seth." This then, would be a question of a physical, bodily resemblance uniting the father and son; the mention of the sexes likewise seems to refer to a physical meaning. But if we apply it to God, such physical resemblance amounts to a gross anthropomorphism (Giesebrecht). Such a way of looking at it is repugnant to the somewhat abstract way of thinking of the author of this narrative. Moreover, the whole of Jahvism abhorred images.

Therefore we must look for a more spiritual resemblance. It is generally admitted that man resembles God through his intellect and his will. God willed to create a being like unto Himself, who would enter into religious contact with Him.[9] However, this kinship should not be taken in a static way, as if man possessed in himself a "divine spark," through which he would by nature partake of the divine perfection. Rather the resemblance is dynamic, in the sense that man, in his personal relationship with other creatures, becomes God's representative. This is explicitly taught in the Book of Wis-

[9] E. Wright, *God Who Acts*, London, 1952, p. 88, note 1— M. Burrows, *An Outline of Biblical Theology*, Philadelphia, 1946, p. 14— B. W. Anderson, *Rediscovering the Bible*, New York, 1951, p. 245.

dom: "God of my fathers, . . . you who . . . in your wisdom have established man to rule the creatures produced by you, to govern the world in holiness and justice," (Wis 9:2). In this *functional* conception of the image of God, man appears as the delegate of his Creator.[10] He is in some way identified with his Lord, since he rules the world in His name: "Let him have dominion over the fish of the sea, the birds of the air, the cattle, over all the wild animals and every creature that crawls on the earth." Insofar as man obeys God's command in the use of the creatures of this earth, he realizes his unity and conformity with God: "What is man that you should be mindful of him, or the son of man that you should care for him? You have made him little less than god (thus in the Hebrew original; the Vulgate, out of reverence for God, reads: 'little less than the angels'), and crowned him with glory and honor. You have given him rule over the works of your hands, putting all things under his feet: all sheep and oxen, yes, and the beasts of the field, the birds of the air, the fishes of the sea, and whatever swims the paths of the seas." (Ps 8:5-9).

Besides this affirmation of man's dignity whereby he is called to be and should try to become ever more God's representative, and even a partner in His spiritual pater-

[10] Cf. the beautiful phrase of W. Zimmerli, *Mose I-II. Die Urgeschichte*, Zurich, 1943, p. 84: "God extends a piece of His royal mantle over the creature, whom He calls to intimacy with Him."—"Co-regency" is a sacred mission, not at all the result of a whimsical choice. To bring out the values of civilization is a strict duty; every act of authority constitutes an order imposed in the name of God Himself.

nity, the sacred text also draws our attention to the bisexual aspect of man: "Male and female he created them." There is no question here of an "androgynous" being, such as we find in Plato's Symposium. But the meaning of the observation is evident: the union of man and woman is the normal way in which man draws nearer to God and fulfills His divine will. K. Barth exaggerates when he claims that the inspired author sees in sexuality as such an element of the quality of being an image of God. But it is manifest that the mention of the two sexes is a reminder that all fertility is a gift of God, and that the propagation of the human race must be considered as a gracious unceasing courtesy of the Divine Creator.[11] To emphasize this thought, the sacred writer points out that God bestows a special blessing: human life, as well as animal life (Gn 1:21), is due to the active intervention of the Creator. It is quite possible also that, in the mind of the ancient author, the perfect parallelism between man and woman is intended to emphasize the equality of both husband and wife, not only in the work of reproduction, but also as God's representatives.

Therefore it seems that the whole passage of Gn 1:26-28 must be interpreted, not in a strictly chronological perspective, as referring to the "first" men in time, but rather *sub specie aeternitatis*, as referring to "everlasting man." This does not mean that the author of Genesis is satisfied to express some other-worldly

[11] T. Maertens, *Les sept jours*, l.c., 61: "God reveals His eternal design to establish a people close to His heart."

doctrine of wisdom, without reference to a beginning or an exact event. On the contrary, by putting the story of creation at the beginning of his history of salvation, he has emphasized and brought out the "dogmatic *fact*" of creation. This means that the *mirabiliter condidisti* of man began at a determined moment of primitive time, "in the beginning," and also that this "wonderful creation" is never stopped. The "first" work of God goes on without ceasing. Even in the description of timeless "human dignity" we detect the exemplification of the original state: what exists now, already existed in the most remote time. God's plan is eternal and traces a unique design.

God, the transcendent Creator, who created the universe by His word alone, that is, without the help of a demiurge, remains forever the first and primitive source of all human dignity. Such is the religious teaching concerning the origin of man, as presented by Gn 1:26-28. No other aspect of this problem—neither the antiquity of man, nor his possible descent from the animal world (not even his superiority over animals),[12] nor the number of first men—is explicitly treated, much less solved. Therefore every attempt at Concordism in this matter is unjustified and is bound to fail. For example, it is vain to interpret the particular intervention of God in the creation of man in the sense of an immediate creation of the human body. The sacred text stands completely apart from scientific transformism; there is nothing to

[12] That superiority stands out better in the text following (Gn 1:28)

prove that the immediate production of the human body adapts itself better to the superiority of man over animals. At any rate, the text, considered objectively, does not lead to any scientific biological conclusion.

2. *Genesis 2:7*

Then the Lord God formed man out of the dust of the ground and breathed into his nostrils the breath of life, and man became a living being.

These words are part of the second account of creation, which serve as an introduction to the narrative of the Fall. The critics attribute this narrative (Gn 2:4—3:24) to an author different from the one who described the work of the Six Days. This explains certain differences between the two narratives, which are, in fact, two parallel and independent accounts.

In Gn 2 creation is presented as the work of God by which He puts an end to a primitive, chaotic situation. This primitive situation, characterized by absolute barrenness, contains three elements: no vegetation, no natural fertilizing water, no man to water the land artificially. In order to relieve this chaos, Yahweh (this is the Hebrew name for God) creates first the man who will water the land, then an abundance of vegetation in Eden, and finally plentiful natural water in the four rivers of Paradise. After this threefold creation, "The Lord God took the man and placed him in the garden of Eden to till it and to keep it." (Gn 2:15).

In this crosswise arrangement (man, whose absence is deplored in the last place, is created first), the origin of man obviously occupies a preponderant place. The concept of "Adam" is again generic; the attention of the author is focused, not on the individual character, but rather on the nature of the first man.

The words "formed out of the dust of the ground" refer to the anthropomorphic representation of the potter molding his material. Furthermore, more than once God is compared with a potter or a modeler (Jer 18:2; Is 45:9). That this is an obvious symbolism was already evident to St. Augustine: "It is a very childish idea that God would have molded man from clay with bodily hands; even if Holy Scripture proposed this, we would have to admit that the author made use of a metaphor, and not that God has limbs as we have . . . Who is stupid enough not to see that the word 'hand' here indicates the power and strength of God?" [13] The image of the potter, as it is used for the Egyptian creator-god Khnûm, suggests the idea of the supreme independence of the Creator. Thus Sirach, among others, explains it in the second century B.C.: "Like clay in the hands of a potter, to be molded according to his pleasure, So are men in the hands of their Creator, to be assigned by him their function." (Sir 33:13). The Hebrew verb "to form" is used by the prophets to indicate the infusion "of the spirit of God." The prophet Zacharia (about 520 B.C.) mentions the "word of the Lord . . . who spreads out the heavens, lays the foundations of the earth, and forms the spirit of man within him:" (Za 12:1). Again this term indicates the "formation" of the light (Is 45:7). This way of using the word "to

[13] Augustinus, *De Genesi ad litteram,* VI, 12, in PL., 34-347

form" shows clearly that it was hardly ever understood in its literal meaning "to mold clay."

The matter from which man is formed is called "dust" from the "ground." The Hebrew name for ground is "adâmâh," and this term is connected with "Adam." In some passages of Scripture the word used in Gn 2:7 does not mean "dust," but rather loose earth, actually the clay used by the potter; here, however, this is not the case. Perhaps the original text may be translated (with Dussaud): "out of fine sand powder." Because he derives from finer material, man would be differentiated from the animals, which have been made out of ordinary, rougher clay (Gn 2:19). In this theory the sacred author might be making use of an ancient myth about the origin of man, in order to express his superiority over the animals.

After having molded the fine dust of the earth, the Creator breathed a breath of life into the nostrils of His creature. The Hebrew word for "breath of life" often means vital power. As God's breath, it proceeds from Him, both in creating and maintaining life. This breath of life, bestowed by God, leaves man again at the moment of death, when he breathes his last breath, his last sigh. Incidentally, it is in the nostrils or the nose that this breath of life is most easily noticed. The expression "every breath of life" frequently means "every living being" (Dt 20:16; Jos 10:40; Is 42:5). The meaning of the image is obvious: the vital power, that unfathomable mystery for which ancient man has a reverential and religious awe, has its origin in God. Because God alone

lives through Himself, all the rest live only through Him. Every life proceeds from the Creator; it is in this sense that Eliu, Job's friend, declares: "For the spirit of God has made me, the breath of the Almighty keeps me alive . . . Behold I, like yourself, have been taken from the same clay by God." (Jb 33:4,6).

Through his life man shares in some way the divine life, which explains his intimacy with God. On the other hand, death is identified with the withdrawal of this breath of life: "If he were to take back his spirit to himself, withdraw to himself his breath, All flesh would perish together, and man would return to the dust." (Jb 34:14-15). And thus the mention of the breath of life in the nostrils refers to the Lord of all life: "For with you is the fountain of life" (Ps 35 (36):10). Man becomes a "living being" only through a wonderful action of the Creator.

Is this breath of life given to man alone, as some commentators hold? Does the expression "living being" mean exclusively a "human personality?" We do not think so. True, this expression does not appear in Gn 2:19 where mention is made of the creation of the animals. But in other passages, the same or similar terms are used of the animals also. Thus Lv 17:11 says in general about man and animal: "the life of a living body is in its blood." [14]

In the face of this simple, yet evocative, narrative of God fashioning a gardener destined for His wonderful garden, we can ask the question which interests us in

[14] P. Denis, l.c., p. 118— E. F. Sutcliffe, l.c., p. 184— M. T. Monroe, *Thinking about Genesis*, London, 1953, p. 167.

this study. Does this narrative contain any positive teaching, either on man's intimate and definitive nature, or on his mode of origin? Do we find here any clear information about the theory of evolution, or about the unicity of the ancestor?

It is clear that the author does not supply an answer to the problem of transformism, for the simple reason that this problem does not fall under his direct consideration. The phrases which he uses point rather to the continual and complete dependence of the earth-born being on his Creator, who has an unrestricted power of disposing of His creature. From the religious point of view, it is completely senseless to wish to resist Him: "Woe to those who would hide their plans too deep for the Lord! . . . Your perversity is as though the potter were taken to be the clay: As though what is made should say of its maker, 'He made me not!' Or the vessel should say of the potter, 'He does not understand.' " (Is 29:15-16; see also Is 45:9 or Sir 10:9). Hence the religious author of Gn 2-3 is not interested in the material cause of the human body (*how* man was created), but rather in the basic religious truth of his "state as a creature" (*of what nature* man was created).[15] St. Paul interprets our passage correctly when he exclaims, "O man, who art thou to reply to God? Does the object moulded say to him who moulded it: Why hast thou made me thus? Or is not the potter master of his clay, to make from the same

[15] P. Denis, l.c., p. 118— W. Zimmerli, *Die Urgeschichte*, Zurich, 1943, p. 137.

mass one vessel for honorable, another for ignoble use?" (Rom 9:20-21; Cf Wis 15:7).

It is certain that the conception of the formation from "the dust of the ground" is more anthropomorphic than that of the creation by the word alone, as told in the first chapter of Genesis. But the fact that the same writer has juxtaposed the two accounts shows sufficiently that the "molding" must not in any case be interpreted materially, and that the "material" element of man does not even come into consideration.

We understand then that the sacred authors who later interpreted Genesis were not at all interested in the question of evolution, nor of the unity of the human race. The formation of man from the dust of the ground applies indeed to the one, individual Adam, but also to the whole of mankind. As an example of the first interpretation we may cite Tob 8:8 (Douay): "Thou madest Adam of the slime of the earth, and gavest him Eve for a helper."[16] As applied to mankind, here is the teaching of Sirach: "So too, all men are of clay, for from earth man was formed" (the Vulgate and the Greek translation read here *Adam* for "man") (Sir 33:10). Job's complaint is significant: "Oh, remember that you fashioned me from clay! Will you then bring me down to dust again?" (Jb 10:9). From these texts it follows that the full attention of the ancient writers is directed to the

[16] The Greek text does not read "of the slime of the earth"; these words are imputed to St. Jerome or perhaps to its Aramean copy. The same Greek text says further: "From these two (Adam and Eve) have issued the whole human race."

fundamental idea of the whole religious attitude, particularly the relationship that unites the weak and perishable human creature to God. The mention of the "dust of the ground," from which man comes and into which he returns (Gn 3:19), cannot really be considered as a reflection upon the material part of man. For death is considered as a manifestation of the natural powerlessness into which man sinks when God "punishes" his sin. In a certain sense man always deserves the name "dust," which is the way God created him: "For he knows how we are formed; he remembers that we are dust," says the Psalmist (Ps 102 (103):14).

In the light of these considerations, it is rather meaningless to ask whether our text is not explained more obviously as implying lifeless, rather than living, matter of the human body before the infusion of the soul. The sacred author does not ask, nor solve, that question, not even "by insinuation." [17]

In the decree of the Pontifical Biblical Commission of June 30, 1909, there is mentioned a "special creation of the first" man. Certain exegetes of Gn 2:7 argue as follows: Since the creation of the soul is common to all men, that which is "special" in the creation of the first man must also extend to his body. However, we may wonder whether the adjective "special" really aims to oppose Adam's case to that of other men. The infusion of a "human" soul transforms the material substratum in every case, and therefore shows a "special" character

[17] A. Jones, *Unless Some Man Show Me*, New York, 1951, p. 92.

when we compare it with the creation of the animals.[18] To declare that the ancient text can be interpreted *only* in a fixed sense (that is, excluding any kind of evolution)[19] is undoubtedly doing violence to it. A moderate transformism (theistic-finalistic, that is, implying the action of a personal God) is neither in agreement nor in disagreement with the text of Gn 2:7.

This same Scripture passage raises other problems too. Does this verse contain a popular teaching about the descent of the human race from a single couple? We do not think so. The author is certainly convinced that only one definite couple was created, but does he "teach" this explicitly? The main point of the teaching about man's total dependence on God is embodied in an event which really happened at the beginning of time. What the book of Isaia says about the people of Israel, describes fairly well the views of the author of Genesis on the original foundation of the history of salvation: "Yet, O Lord, you are our father; we are the clay and you the

[18] L. Pirot, "Adam et la Bible" in *Supplément du Dictionnaire de la Bible*, I, p. 94, remarks that it is a question of the creation of *man*, and not of man's body alone— A similar opinion in P. Heinisch, *Probleme der Urgeschichte*, Luzern, 1947, p. 50.— B. Attout, *Les premières pages de la Bible*, (Brussels, 1933) p. 28, wonders if the term "immediate creation" has perhaps been omitted on purpose.

[19] L. Pirot and P. Cruveilhier, "Genèse (décision de la Commission biblique sur le caractère historique de la . . .)" in *Supplément du Dictionnaire de la Bible*, III (1938), p. 603.— According to E. C. Messenger, *Evolution and Theology*, London, 1931, p. 229, one of the two secretaries of the Biblical Commission who signed the decree of June 30, 1909, namely, Dom Laurent Janssens, O.S.B., has explicitly stated that the formula "peculiaris hominis creatio" was chosen intentionally in order not to exclude a "theistic-finalistic" transformism.

potter: we are *all* the work of your hands." (Is 64:7). Therefore we may conclude with J. Chaine: "Genesis alone does not allow us to give an answer to the question of monogenesis; that answer depends on the teaching of the Church." [20]

Another question concerns the state in which the first man was created. The whole trend of Gn 2 favors the conception of an adult personality. Immediately after his creation, "man" is placed in the Garden of Eden (Gn 2:15); he is old enough to understand God's order as well as His sanction; he realizes the purpose and the meaning of marriage (Gn 2:23-24); he is able, with the complicity of his wife, to commit a serious sin (Gn 3:6, 12,17-19). Likewise the tradition of the Fathers of the Church has in mind an adult, "in his full manliness," as St. Augustine says.[21] On the other hand, it is unquestionable that the sacred author did not intend to give us a strictly genetic account. He simply states the real origin of man in a static form, without reference to a precise chronological sequence. It seems to us that the reflections about the impossibility of the appearance of a "human child" amidst the surrounding animals, have no connection with the intentions of the ancient authors, such as they have been transmitted to us in the inspired texts.

From all this it follows, in our opinion, that in these questions every kind of Concordism is absolutely irrelevant. Yet this rejection of Concordism cannot, as sometimes happens, be thought of as a purely symbolic con-

[20] J. Chaine, *Le livre de la Genèse*, l.c., pp. 54-55
[21] Augustine, *De Genesi ad litteram*, VI, 18, 29, in PL., 34/351

ception of things. The negation of the primeval event, occurring at an irreversible moment of time, seems to us absolutely irreconcilable with the texts. The facts which concern the foundation of our faith are undoubtedly "historic." This does not mean that we can prove them through documents, but simply that they have really taken place. The main question, however, is this: In what way are these facts presented to us? It is well-known that the ancient Fathers of the Church took greater liberty than some modern authors when they considered the relation between "fact" and "presentation of fact." For example, St. Augustine writes this: "In the presence of events, we may wonder whether everything should be understood in a figurative sense *only*, or whether it should *also* be affirmed and upheld that they have really taken place." [22]

What interests the religious author of the Bible, is not the undeniable fact of creation in the remote past, but rather the religious meaning of this primeval event.[23] In the creation of the ancestor, he contemplates, in anticipation, the basic attitude of man as such (as we know him from experience) towards God. This clarification of the intentions of the ancient author has nothing to do with the pursuit of so-called "etiological myths" created by popular imagination. The author of Genesis certainly "teaches" that, from the beginning of time, man was created in divine friendship, and that, deprived of this

[22] Ibid., I, 1, 1, in PL., 34/247

[23] J. Schilderberger, O.S.B., "Die Erzählung vom Paradies und Sündenfall," in *Bibel und Kirche*, 1951, Heft 1 and 2, p. 45.

friendship by sin, he was abandoned to his own weakness. But he presents this fact "in a simple and figurative language, adapted to the mental powers of an imperfectly developed humanity." [24]

If this is so, it is improper to use the imaged, or even "folklorish" [25] presentation of these passages to demonstrate that the theory of the evolution of the human body should be rejected according to the teachings of Gn 2:7. We should always remember that this narrative does not in the least lay claim to being a scientific account.[26] The question of the possibility or probability of evolution must be solved by a considered and prudent science. As long as science is aware of its limits, particularly of its incompetence in the field of specifically philosophical or theological problems, its inquiries will contribute greatly toward working out a complete, accurate, and truly human survey concerning the origin of man.[27]

[24] Letter of the Pontifical Biblical Commission to Cardinal Suhard (January 1948) in *Acta Apostolicae Sedis,* 40 (1948), p. 47.
[25] This word is used by Dom Attout, l.c., p. 40.
[26] Cf. L. Pirot, *Supplément du Dictionnaire de la Bible,* I, p. 94.
[27] If the evolution of the human body were ever scientifically demonstrated, it would be vain to look for a reconciliation of this with Holy Scripture. Such a Concordism would be wrongly prompted by the conviction that natural truth and divine Revelation cannot contradict each other. Not every disagreement necessarily involves a contradiction; this is true only when the "formal object" is the same. In this view, once again, Concordism, conscious or not, is no help to Catholic science.

3. Genesis 2:18–24

Then the Lord God said, "It is not good that the man is alone; I will make him a helper like himself." When the Lord God had formed out of the ground all the beasts of the field and the birds of the air, he brought them to the man to see what he would call them; for that which the man called each of them would be its name. The man named all the cattle, all the birds of the air and all the beasts of the field; but he found no helper like himself. The Lord God cast the man into a deep sleep and, while he slept, took one of his ribs and closed up its place with flesh. And the rib which the Lord God took from the man, he made into a woman, and brought her to him. Then the man said, "She now is bone of my bone, and flesh of my flesh; she shall be called Woman, for from man she has been taken." For this reason a man leaves his father and mother, and clings to his wife, and the two become one flesh.

This popular tale looks like an etiological explanation of the marriage relation between man and woman. The sacred author sees the cause of this relation in the *fact* that, from the beginning, woman was closely connected with "man." The feminine partner is intended for man —by God's Providence—as a "helper like himself." The Hebrew expression refers to a being who can "stand facing the man," as being like him, or "as something which could mirror him, by his reflection." These words relate to exterior sharing (in work, for example) and to material support, but likewise to communion of thought and feelings and to physical union. Sirach comments very correctly: "A wife is her husband's richest treasure, a helpmate, a steadying column." (Sir 36:24)

This partner in the conjugal union goes beyond the level of animals; she is therefore completely human. The author expresses this abstract thought by telling about the creation of animals on the one hand, and about the origin of woman on the other hand. The animals were formed by God from the same dust as man, but yet man is their king. He who imposes a name or knows the name, has power over the being so named. In the first chapter of Genesis God so "names" the light, the firmament, the sea and the land; according to Gn 5, He names "man."

This power (of man over animals) demonstrates the elevation of man above the animals, among which there is no appropriate "mate" for him.

Hence, it is logical that the account of the origin of woman aims to portray the equality between man and woman rather than to emphasize the manner in which she was created. The expression "to be taken from the man" serves to show concretely that the woman possesses a complete human personality.

The image of the "rib" taken from Adam during his mysterious sleep is clearly symbolic. This was already admitted by Origen[28] and by St. Augustine.[29] In the

Middle Ages, too, a few authors had reached the same conclusion, as is evident from a text of Remigius of Saint-Germain in the IXth Century.[30] The symbolic interpretation is very clearly defended by the pen of Cardinal Cajetan (XVIth Century): "The text and the context force me to understand the creation of the woman not in the literal sense, but rather in a mysterious, symbolic sense; not as an allegory, but as a parable." [31] The Hebrew word for "rib" is rather vague; it may also mean "side," for instance of a mountain, of the Ark, of an altar, of a large gate.[32] Moreover the Sumerian word TI (in the language spoken in Mesopotamia before the Semitic conquest) means "life" as well as "rib." For all these reasons we should not insist too much upon the special translation "rib." Incidentally, it is perhaps better to think simply of a real "rib," in accordance with the primitive conception. These parts of the body are fairly close to the heart,[33] and there are enough of them to allow for the removal of one rib, as is proposed in a symbolic representation.

28 Origen, *Contra Celsum,* IV, 38, in PG., 11/1087

29 St. Augustine, *De Genesi contra Manichaeos,* II, 12, 17, in PL., 34/205.

30 Remigius Antissiodorensis, *Commentarius in Genesim,* in PL., 131/63.

31 *Cajetani Commentarii,* I (Lyons, 1639), p. 22. Cajetan has never been condemned for this opinion. No doubt he goes too far when he speaks of a mere "parable."

32 St. Augustine, *De Civitate Dei,* XIV, 23, in PL., 41/430, thinks already that the "side" is intended here: "Eve was made from the side of man;" also in *De Genesi ad litteram,* X, 2, in PL., 34/409.

33 Today the Arabs use the expression: "He is my rib," meaning "he is my true friend."

Whatever may have been the nature of that part of Adam's body which was taken from him, the meaning of the narrative[34] is clear enough: man and woman constitute an indissoluble unity. The woman can be thought of only as a part of the man. By means of this image, three ideas are expressed:

1) The solid bond between husband and wife: "Even thus ought husbands also to love their wives as their own bodies. He who loves his own wife, loves himself. For no one ever hated his own flesh." (Eph 5:28-29);

2) The special dignity of the man: "because a husband is head of the wife" (Eph 5:23). For this reason "woman is the glory of man" (1 Cor 11:7). On the other hand she must be subject to him: "For I do not allow a woman to teach, or to exercise authority over men; but she is to keep quiet. For Adam was formed first, then Eve." (1 Tm 2:12-13);[35]

3) The natural equality between man and woman:[36] "For as the woman is from the man, so also is the man

[34] P. Denis, l.c., p. 130. In the same sense, see H. Lesêtre, "Les récits de l'Histoire Sainte" in *Revue pratique d'Apologétique*, 1906, p. 403.
[35] On this thought, St. Thomas Aquinas indulges in the following considerations: "God did not take Eve from Adam's *head*, because it is not the role of woman to teach man; however he is forbidden to despise her and to treat her as a slave, and that is why she was not formed from his *feet*. But Eve was taken from Adam's *side*, to show that between man and woman there must be a perfect community"; cf. *Summ. Theol.* I, q. 92, art. 3.
[36] This last remark is especially important when we recall that the Oriental often despised woman. Plato too, in regard to his theory of metempsychosis, claims that a guilty soul is reincarnated at first in a woman and then in an animal. Mohammed reserves a place in paradise for his horse, his camel and his cat, but not for any of his wives.

through the woman, but all things are from God." (1 Cor 11:12).[37]

This threefold symbolism (which St. Paul too has foreseen and has applied to *all* husbands and wives), corresponds with the real aim of the sacred author (and therefore of God). It appears clearly in the hymn of joy in which the first man extols the benevolence which God has shown him in the creation of the first woman. God's simple gesture, of bringing the woman to the first man, is the prelude. The "man" recognizes at once (a few authors think: after the first marriage act) the similarity of nature which binds him to the woman "taken from him." The expression, "bone of my bone, and flesh of my flesh" indeed does not prove that the author was thinking of a material rib or of a real equality of nature. In fact it is a much-used metaphor to denote the intimacy of the family bond. Thus Laban says to his nephew Jacob: "You are indeed my flesh and bone." (Gn 29:14). Likewise Abimelech, son of Gedeon, tells his kinsmen in Sichem: "You must remember that I am your own flesh and bone." (Jgs 9:2). All the tribes of Israel say to David at the time of his investiture: "Behold we are thy bone and thy flesh." (2 Kings 5:1) (Douay). And the great king bids the priests Sadoc and Abiathar tell the elders of Juda: "You are my brethren, you are my bone, and my flesh." (2 Kings 19:12) (Douay). The

[37] H. J. T. Johnson, "The Bible, the Church and the Formation of Eve," in *Downside Review*, 69 (1951) pp. 16-24. F. L. Moriarty, "Bulletin of the Old Testament" in *Theological Studies*, 12 (1951), 329 and 331.

term "your own" is used in Is 58:7 to indicate mere fellow-being.

The name of "woman" (virago, L., man-like woman) which "man" assigns to his wife, is due to a play on words and again confirms the symbolic meaning of the account.

When we speak of "symbolism," we do not mean that there is any contradiction between a "symbolic representation" and the accomplishment of a fact in a well-determined moment of time. On the contrary, the reality of the primitive event leads the sacred writer to insert the etiological addition: "For this reason a man leaves his father and mother." The phrase "for this reason" refers to the state of things in the beginning, as Christ recalls it: "Have you not read that the Creator, from the beginning, made them male and female, and said, For this reason a man leaves his father and mother, and clings to his wife, and the two become one flesh?" (Mt 19:4-5).

When man breaks all other bonds and clings in love to his wife, the two become "*one* flesh." This expresses not only the physical reality of marriage but also the more spiritual bond of the family union. The brothers of Joseph say of him: "He is our brother, our own flesh." (Gn 37:27). It is evident that the old inspired author considers sexual love in all its manifestations as a riddle of nature. He detects its deepest foundation in its religious meaning as a "divine mystery." Ultimately this splendid passage of Genesis comes down to this: God approves of sexual love in the monogamous marriage bond: "It is not good that the man is alone." (Gn 2:18).

From the beginning, the family community, which breaks away from the sacred ties of the tribal community, was established by God. This state of affairs is part of God's plan of salvation. Therefore this narrative does not refer to a simple general truth, applying to all men, but without any reference to a single, well-determined fact. No, the historically-minded Hebrew author sees only one explanation of the universally established fact of the marriage bond, namely God's *initial* approbation. Therefore there is in Gn 2:18-24 certainly more than a fable, an allegory or a legend. God brought about a real event, which happened at a certain moment. But this event is the "exemplary" cause of a great number of other similar facts, which have followed in the course of the ages. The first man occupies the first place in the chain of mankind, that is, the place which puts him in the lead. His actions and his gestures are repeated thousands of times; in this sense he is really "the typical man."

This "real" and general event, which happened at the beginning of time, is presented under the form of a popular story. It is by the symbolic presentation of the "historic" seed that the sacred author makes known to all men (starting with the Ancient Near East) God's views on marriage and the family community. The bonds of these institutions are sacred, created by God Himself, and therefore indissoluble.

But a further question arises: "What is the *basic fact* which is affirmed by the sacred author? In other words, how far does symbolism extend?"

The foregoing exegetical notes make it clear that Gn 2:18-24 furnishes no allusion nor any proof which would determine the exact and biological manner in which the "woman" had been "taken" from the man. The inspired author is not in the least interested in such a problem. However, is there any indication that the first woman comes from a real part of the first man? Is not symbolism, which denies such solidarity with material elements, incompatible with the decree of the Biblical Commission of June 30, 1909? That decree ranks "the fact that the first woman was formed from the first man" among the "facts concerning the foundations of the Christian religion." We believe it can be demonstrated that this incompatibility is non-existent.

We would undoubtedly commit a grave error to deny that this narrative refers to a real event: the etiological explanation given in the text implies a real beginning—at the dawn of time—of the eternal symbolism. Therefore we may accept the conclusion of H. Junker: "The opinion previously defended (about the symbolic character of the rib) does not conflict with the decisions of the Biblical Commission. To express our thought clearly, we consider as a symbolic representation only the *manner* in which the creation of Eve is described; we do not deny that this 'formation of the first woman from the first man' is a fact." [38]

[38] H. Junker, *Die biblische Urgeschichte*, Bonn, 1932, p. 43 ff.

How must we understand this symbolically-expressed fact? It seems to us inadmissible to consider as facts the details of such a symbolic representation; precisely in this case we scarcely consider their symbolic character. This is what happens when we interpret literally the inspired words "She shall be called Woman, *for from man she has been taken.*" (Gn 2:23).[39] By retaining the figurative meaning of symbolic details, we easily explain the fact that the woman was taken from the man not as a material fact, but rather as a spiritual reality. The story of the rib does not symbolize a purely biological formation from a material part of the man, but it suggests and represents a reality that projects beyond matter. The content of this "human" and spiritual reality is that man (the first man, and all the others after him) is not complete without his "better half." Something is lacking in him, and he can find it in the marriage bond to which God Himself destines him. True, this mutual completion occurs also in the physical order; but the symbolism of the biblical author scarcely emphasizes the bodily aspect of the story which unites woman to man from the beginning.

Does not this interpretation conflict with the phrase: "the *formation* of the first woman *from* the first man?" Not necessarily, for the preposition *from* does not specially indicate a material causality. It harmonizes perfectly with an exemplary and final causality:[40] man is

[39] A. Bea, *Il problema antropologico in Gen. 1-2.* Il trasformismo, Rome, 1950, p. 52.
[40] Cf. H. Lusseau, *Précis d'histoire biblique,* Paris, 1948, pp. 55-56.

the intrinsic meaning and the objective destination of woman. Granting that, in the last analysis, the aim of the narrative is to convey a few basic and very important religious truths, everything which serves this purpose may be considered as symbolic (we do not say: unreal). This symbolism applies also to the *fact* that the woman was taken from the man. This fact need not necessarily be conceived materially, but it applies to the real relationship (dating from a well-determined moment of time, and since then continuing forever), of woman to man, as to her prototype and her life's purpose.[41]

If the above observations are correct, it follows that certain Concordistic speculations about the way in which Eve was taken from Adam's body, are inadmissible. These speculations are altogether meaningless. Holy Scripture does not want to tell us anything about the genetic derivation of the female body from the male body.[42] For example, the theory of Adam's "vision," by which he would have understood the deep meaning of what God was working in him, has absolutely no support in the text. The sacred author—led by his etiological preoccupation—simply projects "backwards in time" what he ascertains in the normal marriage status. He feels no interest in purely biological questions. On the contrary, his theological conception of marriage merely

41 H. Lesêtre, l.c., p. 403. "Adam and Eve are two beings of the same nature, whom one same affection must unite, since Eve is for Adam another self."

42 Cf. the wise words of St. John Chrysostom: "About this you know nothing. He alone knows it, who has performed the creation . . . (15th homily on Gn 2, n.2, in PG., 53/121)— Cf. P. Heinisch, l.c., p. 55.

emphasizes the fact that the woman is destined for the man (so it is for the first woman and the first man, and for all wives toward their husbands). God Himself established this community of life; and therefore it is perfectly and primitively good.

Any exegesis which takes literally the anthropomorphic representation of God's surgical intervention seems inadmissible to us. The mythological explanation, which thinks it discovers in the ancient narrative a hermaphroditic or androgynous legend, merits no further consideration. Yet, looking at it more closely, this mythological interpretation—which we do not endorse—helps us to better understand the symbolism with which the sacred author's mentality is filled. At any rate, it is this symbolism which gives meaning to the fact of the union between man and woman, which took place in most remote time. It is not imposed on the narrative from without, but it is part of the primitive event. The state of the first human beings, who were united in married love, finds its continuation in all similar states.

A final question in connection with Gn 2:18-24 concerns the unity of the human race. To be sure, the most obvious and most natural explanation seems to be that of the ancient author who identifies the "woman" with the one individual Eve. Yet it is important to remember that in the Genesis account the two individuals, the man and the woman, cannot be considered as being completely isolated from other men. On the contrary, in some way they include all the others. The text of Gn 2:18-24 certainly goes beyond the horizon of a single couple, and as such it is hardly apt to give an answer to the problem of the number of first human beings.[43] The whole attention of this narrative, directed entirely toward religious considerations, is fixed on the connection uniting man to God, and, within humanity, man to woman. All society proceeds ultimately from God Himself, and that from the beginning of time. Whatever goes beyond the aims of this doctrine is perhaps not false; the author admits it more or less consciously, but it is not the direct object of his affirmation.[44] Therefore we have no right, when using the ancient text (taken by itself, leaving out of account the subsequent traditional explanations or the authentic declarations of the Church) to conclude that the author infallibly affirms what he could not have intended to say.

On the whole, all that we can infer from the text is the unicity of an event which happened at the beginning of time. This single event is the bearer of a religious symbolism, extending to all mankind. As for the unicity of a single primitive couple, it does not seem to be the object of an explicit and direct affirmation.

[43] H. Lesêtre, l.c., p. 104. "In considering the Genesis narrative, it does not seem that there would be any absolute reason to connect all human descent to Adam and Eve."
[44] A. M. Dubarle, *Les Sages d'Israël*, Paris, 1946, p. 21.

4. *Romans 5:12–19*

Therefore as through one man sin entered into the world and through sin death, and thus death has passed unto all men because all have sinned—for until the Law sin was in the world, but sin is not imputed when there is no law; yet death reigned from Adam until Moses even over those who did not sin after the likeness of the transgression of Adam, who is a figure of him who was to come. But not like the offense is the gift. For if by the offense of the one the many died, much more has the grace of God, and the gift in the grace of the one man Jesus Christ, abounded unto the many. Nor is the gift as it was in the case of one man's sin, for the judgment was from one man unto condemnation, but grace is from many offenses unto justification. For if by reason of the one man's offense death reigned through the one man, much more will they who receive the abundance of the grace and of the gift of justice reign in life through the one Jesus Christ. Therefore as from the offense of the one man the result was unto condemnation to all men, so from the justice of the one the result is unto justification of life to all men. For just as by the disobedience of the one man the many were constituted sinners, so also by the obedience of the one the many will be constituted just.

In the debate about the origin of man, we call on several texts of the New Testament. We mention especially

Chapter 5 of the Epistle to the Romans, with the famous parallel of the two Adams.

We should first remark that of the three problems mentioned above, only one is considered in this passage. No mention is made here of the age of mankind, nor of the bodily evolution of man. Only the problem of monogenesis should be considered here.

An attentive reading of Rom 5:12-19 brings out at once the repeated mention of the unicity of the first as well as of the second Adam: "through one man sin entered into the world" (v.12), "by the offense of the one the many died" (v.15), "For if by reason of the one man's offense death reigned through the one man" (v.17), "by the disobedience of the one man the many were constituted sinners" (v.19). It is clear that the most obvious explanation of these texts conceives the joint responsibility in Adam (the transmission of a state of sin) as dependent on the physical solidarity of the human race.

It is possible that, metaphysically speaking, all human solidarity in the material order is ultimately based upon bodily reproduction. But it is important to examine whether the text of St. Paul is totally explained by this physical reproduction, and if we really understand the Apostle's meaning when we stop at that idea.

Should we interpret the fact that all men are included or understood in Adam in a material or in a spiritual sense? According to the Apostle, it is certain that the *first sin* becomes an inherited sin. In this perspective, the first individual sinner, instead of being contrasted to and distinct from the multitude of other men, rather contains them in himself. Perhaps we are too prone to stress the *contrast* between the one Adam and the numerous sinners. We tend to forget too easily that universal sin entered the world, not only because Adam was the cause of it, but likewise *by the very fact* that he has sinned. The unicity of the first sinner, as opposed to the multiplicity of sinners influenced by him, seems less important than the fact that he contains them all within himself in a mysterious way.

St. Paul shows that he was thinking this way when he speaks of Christ of whom "Adam is a figure." (v.14). As St. Leo puts it concisely, the Apostle demonstrates that "what has fallen in the first Adam, has been redressed in the second." [45] In Christ the gifts of grace are poured out over all men, because Christ contains all men in Himself; the solidarity makes possible the substitution of Christ for us, not the other way around. Redemption, which Christ brings abundantly, justifies all men thoroughly and fundamentally: "grace is from many offenses unto justification." (v.16).[46] Likewise, by the fault of Adam, "the many died" (v.15),[47] that is, by the very fact that there has been a "first" sin, the tyranny of sin has been definitely established, and all men are condemned: "the judgment was from one man unto

[45] PL., 54/168.
[46] Cf. 2 Cor 5:14: "since one died for all, therefore all died."
[47] Cf. also 1 Cor 15:22: "For as in Adam all die, so in Christ all will be made to live." Remarkable in this text is the lack of emphasis upon "one"; the text mentions (without article) "a *man*" (1 Cor 15:21).

condemnation" (v.16). There can be no doubt that the unicity of the first sin is affirmed; the state of sin of all mankind is bound to one single transgression.

But, we may ask, how must we understand this connection between the state of sin of mankind and the first act of sin? Does the one transgression necessarily imply one individual transgressor? It seems to us that for St. Paul this question is of secondary importance. The main point is that the common state of sin has been "caused" in a rather extrinsic way by an isolated individual. It is really the affirmation of a mysterious identity. All men sin *in Adam*, and it is through his disobedience (*ipso facto*, and not merely by way of consequence) that all men sin, that "the many were constituted sinners" (v.19).

For the individualistic way of thinking, the unicity of the transgression spontaneously suggests the unicity of one single individual sinner. The latter communicates his guilt to other individuals, doubtless bound to him, but nevertheless strictly distinct from him. For St. Paul, on the contrary, the solidarity was much greater. His thought is not so much along the limits of a temporal succession of different individuals; but rather it fits the lines of a timeless perspective: (Through the first sin) "death has passed unto all men" (v.12).[48]

As a result of a merely individualistic interpretation of the figure of Adam, many commentators identify the causal relation between Adam and other men as the chronological succession of physical descent. About this interpretation, we must remark first that it explains, at

[48] Cf. Nm 15:26; Dt 13:13-16.

the very most, how the nature was inherited, but not how the state of guilt was transmitted. Furthermore, there may be other ways of explaining this causality (or rather this inclusion). This is what already results from the causal relationship which unites all men with Christ. This relationship is certainly neither physical nor genetic; and yet, according to Rom 5:15-16, it is much stronger than our relation to Adam.[49] Christ is certainly the Head of the Mystical Body, but He is in no way the "father" of the new humanity, except in a very weak and figurative sense.

We might perhaps find an explanation of this mysterious inclusion of all human beings in Adam, as well as in Christ, in the concept of the so-called "corporate personality." [50] Very often the Bible mentions a community —a city, a tribe, a clan, a family—whose dead or living members act as one individual, through one member who is considered as the representative of the whole group. H. Wheeler Robinson, the English author, who has elaborated this notion, enumerates three important properties in it: 1. the "corporate personality" contains the past and the future. For instance, a people is identified with its ancestors (cf. Am 3:1); "to destroy Achab" is "to strike the descendants of Achab" (4 Kgs 10:17); the male descendants perpetuate the "name," that is the person himself (2 Sm 18:18). 2. This personality consti-

[49] St. Augustine, for instance, teaches that Christ and the faithful constitute "one man" (PL., 34/266), "one and the same person" (PL., 34/88), "one Christ" (PL., 39/1500), "one total Christ" (PL., 36/662).
[50] Cf. J. DeFraine, S.J., *Adam et son lignage*, Studies on the idea of "corporate personality" in the Bible, Desclée De Brouwer, Paris, 1959.

tutes a concrete being. It is not an idea or a literary personification, but a real entity. Daniel, for instance, symbolizes the people (the "holy people of the Most High") by the individual figure of "the son of man" (Dn 7:13, 27). Jesus also has used the same title, thereby indicating perhaps that all His own people constitute a "mystical" unity with Him. 3. The corporate personality and the group to which it corresponds, are easily blended and mutually substituted. The nation is often represented by an individual figure; very often a minority symbolizes a whole group.

The importance of this idea of "corporate personality" for the interpretation of many biblical texts is obvious. If an entire community can be presented, in a concentrated way, as a single individual, that is exactly what St. Paul, it seems, wishes to teach us in the passage in which we are interested. His main assertion emphasizes the fact that Adam and Christ are, in a mysterious way, "several." The solidarity of the human community with Christ is so great, that the death and the resurrection of the Head is shared by the Body, which, in a certain sense, dies and rises from the dead with its Head. As for Adam, the physical bond which is the result of bodily propagation does not seem to be affirmed *in recto*. The emphasis is not upon an uninterrupted chain of bodily generations, but rather upon the fact that the

whole malice of inherited sin was already really present in the first sin.[51] The death and the triumph of Christ are

[51] St. Irenaeus, *Adversus Haereses,* V, 16,3, in PG., 7/1168: "*We* offended God in the first Adam, by refusing to carry out His com-

in a certain sense collective; the sin of Adam is also collective, potentially at the beginning of time, actually throughout the course of history.

There are cases where obviously the solidarity between one individual and a group excludes physical descent. When St. Paul says that "they are not all Israelites who are sprung from Israel; nor because they are the descendants of Abraham, are they all his children" (Rom 9:6-7), he adds: "they are not sons of God who are the children of the flesh, but it is the children of promise who are reckoned as posterity." (v.8). Therefore St. Paul admits that one can be a "son of Abraham," without any bodily descent from him. Perhaps we have understood the connection of all men with Adam in a one-sided physical sense. Perhaps we have thus overlooked other possible ways of explaining the inclusion of all human beings in Adam as directly affirmed by St. Paul. Among these other possible ways we may mention: the influence exercised by a privileged person, only because he is first in a chain, which is not necessarily a physical chain; a juridical transference of powers or rights; and finally the idea of participation proper to a whole "corporate personality."

If we take these possibilities into consideration, it seems we must reach the following conclusion: from the text of Rom 5:12-19, taken exactly, we can hardly deduce an indisputable argument for the monogenetic

mands."—St. Basil the Great uses this formula: "We were dead in Adam" (PG., 32/969); and St. Athanasius says explicitly, in his *Oratio prima contra Arianos*, 51 (PG., 26/117): "As through Adam's sinning, sin passed into all men . . ."

descent of man.[52] St. Paul refers simply to the account of the first sin as given in Genesis. He "teaches" nothing explicit about the strictly individual unicity of the first sinner. The original "man" sinner is designated by the apostle with the name of "Adam" which is used also in Gn 2-3. St. Paul's whole attention is focused, not upon the unicity of this individual sinner, but on the unicity of the original sin which has become common to all,—not on an ancestor numerically one, but on the "corporate" character of the first "man." [53]

The following objection could be raised: "The absolute unity of Christ underlines the unity of Adam, and the impossibility of imagining several incarnated Christs forces us, by analogy and symmetry, to admit the impossibility of a plurality in Adam." [54] This objection would be perfectly valid if we denied the reality of the single sin committed "in the beginning." But we have seen that this is incompatible with the real trend of the account of the fall. In reality there is only one fall, as there is only one redemption. But, just as this redemption was brought to men thanks to the one Christ who contains "the multitude," so sin and death were introduced into the world by the one Adam, who also represents all mankind in himself. The unicity refers in some

[52] J. Levie, "Les limites de la preuve d'Ecriture sainte en Théologie" in: *Nouvelle Revue Théologique*, 1949, 1009-1029.

[53] Compare 1 Cor 15:49: "Therefore, even as we have borne the likeness of the earthy, let us bear also the likeness of the heavenly."

[54] J. Guitton, *Le développement des idées dans l'Ancien Testament*, Aix-en-Provence, 1947, p. 228.

way to universal human malice, concentrated in the first sinner.

Looking at it closely, the figure of Adam appears in a rather allegorical context.[55] Rom 5:12-19 mentions the personification of "death" (v.17), of sin which entered into the world (v.12), and of the Law, which intervened here (v.20). It is precisely because Adam was more than an isolated individual sinner, that he could be a type of Christ. The latter also was more than one unique man; He was, to tell the truth, simply the Man (representative) who contains all others.[56]

The exegesis of Rom 5:12-19 authorizes us to believe that this study does not consider the problem of monogenesis directly and explicitly. Under these conditions, it is difficult to expect a solution therein.

[55] Cf. J. Levie, l.c., p. 1019.

[56] Cf. 1 Tm 2:5, "himself man, Christ Jesus"— Cf. J. M. Lagrange, *Saint Paul, Epître aux Romains,* Paris, 1916, p. 118.

5. *Acts 17:26*

And from one man he has created the whole human race and made them live all over the face of the earth, determining their appointed times and the boundaries of their lands.

In his famous discourse before the Areopagus, St. Paul explains to the Athenians, "the most religious of men," the worshippers of the "unknown God," his Christian view of the divine nature. God is the Lord of Heaven and of earth, Who bestows life, breath and all things on all His creatures. He has produced, from one single source, the whole human race to make them live on the whole earth.

The Greek text presents a rather puzzling expression: "from only one." Should we insert: "from one father," "from one man," "from one source," or perhaps "from one blood"? For those who think that they may rely on the obvious explanation of Rom 5:12-19, and on the mention of the "*whole* human race," the answer is "from one man." Nevertheless certain manuscripts, as well as quotations from the Fathers of the Church (from the second century, with St. Ireneus), read: "from one blood." We may consider here the expression in the Prologue of St. John: "to be born of blood." In the Old Testament the "blood" was considered as the bearer of the soul and of life; therefore "to be born of one blood" would mean: to belong to the same human descent.

According to this last interpretation, St. Paul directly

affirms the brotherhood of men and of all peoples. Therefore the apostle seems to want to attack the pride of the Athenians, who boasted of being an indigenous race, entirely different from the surrounding "barbarians." [57]

Doesn't St. Paul intend to prove the unicity of God through the unicity of the human race, which he has previously affirmed? In doing this, he rejects the opinion of the Greeks and of the Ancients in general, which holds that each people, and even each city, descended from its own divinity. But, if all men have been created by God, it is a proof that there is only one God. In this way all the gods of paganism fall into nothingness.

The Greeks already admitted the unity of the human race. But St. Paul undoubtedly has the spirit of the texts of the Old Testament, such as Gn 1:27 or Dt 32:8. In that case we do not have the right to infer from his affirmation an argument to prove that the whole human race descends from one single man. The apostle does not seem to be concerned about that question. His main thesis concerns the unity of God, and the brotherhood of men. Therefore it is difficult to hail in Acts 17:26 an "unshakeable scriptural foundation" of monogenesis.[58] The *peak* of St. Paul's reasoning emphasizes the vocation of all men to "seek God." This God is the unique and universal Father of all races and all peoples. (Acts 17:28). Therefore the teaching of v. 17:26 certainly does not concern the historical unicity of one single

[57] Cf. Cicero, *Pro Flacco*, 26, 62.
[58] J. Renié, l.c., p. 108.

ancestor, but rather the lofty destination of man. Indeed all human beings have been created in order to turn towards one God who "is not far from any one of us." (Acts 17:27).

III *The Teachings of the Church*

IN THE EYES of Catholics, the Church alone has the requisite authority to interpret authentically the meaning of the biblical narratives. Therefore we must compare the exegesis of the texts explained previously with the requirements of "the analogy of faith." This term indicates the inner harmony of revealed truths with one another. The inspired books cannot give place to an explanation which would conflict with a doctrine guaranteed by the Church. This principle is justified by the fact that Revelation, the work of the God of truth, must bear the mark of that same truth. By virtue of an obvious dogmatic postulate, Revelation must be distinguished by the harmonious unity of all its component elements. Therefore the Catholic exegete must reject every interpretation of Holy Scripture which would imply a contradiction of the sacred books with each other, or which would be incompatible with other teachings of the Church. In a word, he must take into consideration the Tradition of the Church, which has crystallized around definite scriptural texts. That applies especially to the texts which have been, so to speak, canonized, that is, the explanation of which has been solemnly imposed.[1] But there are also other cases where certain passages have received a properly traditional exegesis, though it can't be called a strictly authentic interpretation.

Should, for instance, the doctrine of the Church explicitly condemn polygenesis, it is evident that a polygenetic explanation of the scriptural texts could not be accepted by a Catholic. The case is quite different, of course, when, in the absence of any such formal censure, the polygenetic explanation is envisaged, not as the only possible hypothesis, but only as a hypothesis which should not be rejected à priori. It is certain that a text, taken literally, cannot mean more than what the author, even the inspired author, has objectively expressed in it. Therefore, if the literal meaning of the words implies that the author is not making a direct pronouncement on a given problem, it is vain to look for a decisive argument in his text. Catholic exegesis cannot take advantage of the practice, well-intentioned though it may be, of reading into the texts what, objectively, is not there. St.

[1] As J. Levie, l.c., p. 1017, remarks, it is explicitly stated in the Encyclical *Divino afflante* that there are only a very few texts whose meaning has been "dogmatized."

Augustine had already written: "We should not want the sense of Scripture to agree with our own conviction, but rather that our thought agree with that of Scripture."[2] It is undeniable that a theologian who keeps abreast of the progress of Revelation, may assemble in a synthetic survey the different texts which are scattered over the course of history. He may even examine them in the light of those doctrines of the Church which are not contained in written books. But in that case, it seems he goes beyond a simple commentary and adorns the ancient texts with a substantially new contribution.

In the question which interests us here, we draw attention to three kinds of teachings. 1. Either we may claim that monogenesis is implicitly contained in the solemnly defined article of faith concerning original sin; 2. or we may argue that the ordinary teaching of the Church imposes monogenesis; 3. or again, that certain recently promulgated documents define the position of the Church in this matter in a clear and unambiguous way. We must now examine more closely each of these three views of the doctrine of the Church.

[2] St. Augustine, *De Genesi ad litteram,* in PL., 34/260

1. The Doctrine of Original Sin

In a well known article from the monumental *Dictionnaire de Théologie Catholique*, two priest brothers asked the following question: "Could not original sin have been the act of a more or less numerous collectivity, instead of being that of one single couple? In the two cases, would not the whole of humanity descend from these first sinners?" [3] In order to decide whether such a view of original sin is acceptable, we must examine whether or not it contains any essential modification of the dogma. Now a certain number of theologians feel that to admit polygenesis is to introduce a substantial alteration into the doctrine.[4]

If we admit the creation of several couples in different places and at different times, it seems there were also several falls into sin. But is such a thing really possible? Must not the unicity of the first fault, that fundamental datum of the Christian faith, be necessarily guaranteed by the unicity of the first sinner?

Let us consider the problem concretely, by placing before us the most widely held scientific hypothesis of monophyletic polygenesis. Is it possible, in that hypothesis, to admit that *all* of these original human beings would have been guilty of a grave sin? Can we imagine that a more or less great multitude, enjoying holiness

3 A. and J. Bouyssonie, under the word "Polygénisme," in *Dictionnaire de Théologie Catholique*, XII, 2536.
4 Cf. H. Lennerz, "Quid theologo dicendum de polygenismo? in *Gregorianum*, 29 (1948) pp. 417-434.

and original justice, would have sunk into sin en masse?[5] Let us add that this collective fall could have been only an effect of the freedom of each one. How then can we imagine a unanimity of collaboration in evil in a multitude inevitably dispersed in time and space? At *what moment* had the fall, the original cause of transmitted sin, been terminated? What would have happened before the entire completion of the first sin, at the moment, for example, when some human beings would have already committed a real sin, and others not yet? Would the several couples have waited for each other before bringing children into the world? Did the children of those who had already begotten them remain free from hereditary sin?

When we consider the problem *concretely*, we see that the unity of the fall leads irresistibly to the unicity of the first sinner. So a proponent of polygenesis faces the following dilemma: either to divide the unity of the original sin, or to repudiate its universality. In both cases he alters an essential point of the doctrine of the Church.

The reasoning outlined above, which holds that it is difficult to deny the individual character of Adam, seems to be based on the conviction that original sin, as inherent in human nature, has been transmitted by way of generation. What is the *dogmatic* teaching of the Church on this point?

Theologians generally admit that generation plays a

[5] Ch. Hauret, l.c., p. 176.

decisive role in the diffusion of original sin. They estimate that the transmission of the sin of Adam must follow the same channel as that by which the whole of humanity is united with the life of its first ancestor. In order to defend their position, these theologians appeal to the texts of the Council of Trent, in which the infallible assembly has solemnly proclaimed its faith in the dogma of original sin: "The word of the Apostle 'through one man sin entered into the world and through sin death, and thus death has passed unto all men because all have sinned' (Rom 5:12), may be understood only in the way in which the Catholic, universal Church has always understood it. It is on these grounds and in accordance with this rule of faith, that, according to the tradition of the apostles, even little children, who are incapable of any personal sin, are nevertheless duly baptized for the remission of sin. In this way what they have acquired by generation is erased in them by regeneration. For 'unless a man be born again of water and the Spirit, he cannot enter into the kingdom of God' (Jn 3:5)." [6]

We must now make an objective analysis of this solemn declaration of the great Council. For this purpose we may refer to the rules of interpretation employed in the Church, as well as to the minutes of the Assembly.

First let us note that in every dogmatic canon, that is, in every declaration concerning a point of faith, the denial of which falls under the anathema ("anathema sit"), only that which is explicitly and directly ("in

[6] Council of Trent, Fifth Session, Canon 4. Cf. Denzinger-Bannwart-Umberg, *Enchiridion Symbolorum*, n. 791.

recto") asserted, is infallibly defined. The arguments invoked (here, for example, the mention of Rom 5:12) are not infallibly affirmed.[7]

The important part of the phrase: "In this way, what (little children) have acquired by generation is erased in them by regeneration," was worked out in the discussions which took place at the Council of Trent, from May 25 to June 17, 1546. It refers to the opinion of Pelagius, the fourth century heretic, who was condemned on May 1, 418, by 200 bishops in the 16th Council of Carthage,[8] because he denied a strict relation of causality between the first sinner, Adam, and all other sinners. Pelagius claimed that these sinners had acted only through an extrinsic "imitation" of Adam ("imitatione"), and had not incurred any intrinsic guilt already present at birth ("generatione").[9] We must therefore understand in the same way the terms used in the abovementioned canon; what the Council affirms is that, *as a result* of the first sin, all men who are born enter into the world with a guilt of sin, which must be erased or eliminated by the baptism of regeneration.

Does the Council declare, by the same act, that the guilt of sin is transmitted by means of bodily generation? The canons undoubtedly return frequently to the idea that not only the punishment of sin, but also the

[7] According to C. J. Hefele, *Histoire des Conciles*, X, 1 (transl. A. Michel), Paris, 1938, p. 49, a few of the Fathers of the Council tried, in vain, to have accepted as of faith a canon declaring explicitly: "Whoever denies that Paul, in Rom 5, speaks of original sin, let him be anathema."

[8] Denzinger, n. 102.

[9] Cf. also Canon 3 in Denzinger, 790.

guilt itself has been transmitted, or "transfused" ("transfudisse") [10] to Adam's "posterity" ("propago").[11] Very surely there exists a causal relation between Adam and all little children who "share something of the original sin of Adam."[12] Nevertheless, since the Acts of the Council reveal that the problem was not treated in detail, we cannot depend on the formula "generatione contrahere" to discern bodily generation as part of the dogma. We can only declare that: "At birth, man incurs a guilt which is due to Adam's sin."

We have said that the Council does not seem to have considered the transmission of original sin through physical generation as a point in which dogma is directly interested. There was no argument at Trent about the fact of the transmission of Adam's sin to all the children of men: that fact is clearly proposed as a revealed truth. Furthermore, there was no discussion raised among the Fathers of the Council about the manner in which this transmission is accomplished, but others gave reasons for this unanimity of viewpoint. Practically everyone was convinced, *without giving it a thought*, that original sin was transmitted through natural generation.

However, the Council rejected the following formula, in which the bishop of Accia (on the island of Corsica), Benedictus dei Nobilis, wanted to draw attention to the concrete process of generation: "(Original sin implies) a taint and a corruption of generation, which every man

[10] Canon 3: "transfusum."

[11] Canon 2, Denzinger 788. Cf. already Augustine, in PL., 44/612—and Denzinger 175, the 2nd Council of Orange (anno 529), canon 2.

[12] Canon 4, Denzinger, 791.

acquires from his parents and which are inherent in his flesh."[13] Hence, it is certain that the Fathers of the Council did not stress the *bodily aspect* of the transmission. What is truly important in their eyes is outlined in the formula of St. Leo the Great: "Little children are guilty of Adam's sin and are, as it were, imprisoned in that sin."[14] When we mention "human *nature* injured in Adam" by sin, and when we explain the meaning of the word "nature" as bodily generation, we advance, actually, a *theological explanation*, whose only purpose is to depict, more accurately perhaps, the dogmatically certain inclusion of all men in Adam. The purely dogmatic position is penetratingly condensed in the formula of the Conventual monk Cornelius Mussus of Piacenza, bishop of Bitonto: "All of us were in Adam when he sinned, before we were born; when we are born, Adam is in us; similarly, when Christ suffered for us, all of us were in Him, and thus our sins were taken away by Him."[15] Finally it is interesting to note that the Council did not take into consideration the following proposal of an explicit definition: "If anyone denies that the taint of original sin is transmitted to the children of the faithful by means of bodily generation, let him be anathema."[16]

Since the Council itself has not wished to formally establish the dogmatic character of the bodily method of the inclusion of all men in Adam, isn't it legitimate to admit that the physical transmission, by means of genera-

[13] Cf. S. Ehses, *Concilii Tridentini actorum*, Freiburg, 1911, V. 205.
[14] Leo Magnus, *Epistola 84 ad Aquil. episc.* in PL., 54/593.
[15] S. Ehses, l.c., V, 175.
[16] S. Ehses, l.c., V, 198.

tion, does not belong directly to the elements of the dogma? What is strictly defined at Trent, was already forcefully expressed in the sentence of St. Ambrose: "All of us have sinned in the first man . . . hence Adam is in each one of us." [17] Nevertheless, even if in all probability the physical or bodily transmission of sin is not directly a part of revealed dogma, a transmission under that form seems to be the most obvious one. Hence we can understand that an opinion which excludes such a transmission (in the case of polygenesis or even monophyletism) is considered not very compatible with dogma. If we deny theological monogenesis, the transmission of original sin is in danger of being denied too. Therefore we consider the denial of the descent of mankind from one single couple as at least temerarious.[18] However, to our mind, it is an exaggeration to claim that polygenesis "smacks of heresy," or that monogenesis is "implicitly revealed." [19]

[17] Ambrosius, *Apologia prophetae David*, II, 12, 71, in PL., 14/915.
[18] Msgr. Amann, under the word "Transformisme" in *Dictionnaire de Théologie Catholique*, XV, 1390.
[19] J. Renié, l.c., p. 110.

2. *The Ordinary Teaching of the Church*

Some authors are of the opinion that at least the ordinary teaching of the Church teaches monogenesis as a safe doctrine.[20] To prove it, they refer to a project of a dogmatic definition which had been worked out at the first Vatican Council (1869-1870). As we know, the Fathers of that Council were forced by circumstances to separate before being able to issue a certain number of definitions. The text which interests us is part of the 15th chapter of the Constitution *Dei Filius*. But only the first four chapters of that constitution were proclaimed as dogmas. Here is the proposed diagram: "Guided by the revelation of the Old and of the New Testament, we profess and teach that the whole human race finds its origin in one single ancestor, Adam . . . Moreover, should this truth be denied, other dogmas will also be threatened: the spreading of original sin from the first individual man to all other men, and the redemption of all men by the one Mediator between God and men, Christ Jesus . . . Hence we condemn under penalty of anathema the error which denies the unity and the common origin of the whole human race." Certainly this document deserves the fullest attention, and it expresses a teaching generally accepted at the time it was elaborated. Nevertheless, it is an undeniable fact that the diagram has never been proclaimed a dogma. True, this

20 R. Garrigou-Lagrange, "Le monogénisme n'est-il nullement révélé, pas même implicitement?" in *Doctor Communis*, 2 (1948), pp. 191-202.

text expresses to some extent, the ordinary teaching of the Church; but, as it stands (as an undebated project), it is devoid of all juridical authenticity.

The unity of the human race or the descent of all men through bodily generation are very rarely mentioned in the liturgy of the Mass and of the Sacraments. The few allusions in the antiphons, the responses and the lessons constitute a foundation too insecure to clearly establish the doctrine of the Church from the "law of prayer."

In the Catechisms, authentic accounts of the ordinary teaching of the Church, the unicity of our first parents is not explicitly taught. It is everywhere assumed; but nowhere is it imposed in precise terms.

3. Explicit Teachings

In the question of man's origin, a Catholic must also be guided by certain explicit declarations emanating from the teaching authority of the Church. Here are some of them which we shall examine.

Fifty years ago much importance was attached to a canon of the provincial Council of Cologne (1860), whose decrees had been approved by the Holy See: "Our first parents were directly created by God. Hence we declare to be in contradiction with Holy Scripture and with the Faith the opinion of those who do not hesitate to affirm the spontaneous evolution of an imperfect nature towards a more perfect and closely allied form, from which man would finally have developed, at least insofar as his body is concerned.[21] Undoubtedly this condemnation was directed first against materialistic evolutionism; but "theistic transformism" also seems to have been aimed at. To be sure, there was no infallible declaration of the Church; nevertheless a few works of Catholic writers advocating a mitigated transformism, were censured by the Holy Office.[22] It is hardly probable, however, that, at the present time, the ecclesiastical authorities would take similar measures.

On June 30, 1909, the Pontifical Biblical Commission issued the decree already mentioned previously, which sets down among the "points concerning the founda-

21 *Collectio Lacensis,* V, 292.

22 These were the books of P. Leroy, O.P., *L'évolution restreinte des espèces organiques,* 1891, and of P. Zahn, O.P., *Evolution and Dogma,* Chicago, 1896.

tion of the Christian religion," the "special creation of man," the fact that "the first woman was formed from the first man," and "the unity of the human race." [23] We have already discussed the first two points. As for the unity of the human race, this point is certainly asserted in Holy Scripture. All men who are born now, were mysteriously present in the first sinner. The question remains of finding out if this last point is to be taken in the sense of a strict unicity, or of a multiplicity including all mankind. The most natural and spontaneous conception will simply connect the unity of the human race with the idea of only one individual couple. The latter is supposed to spread out by the process of generation, in order to reach the present state of mankind.

In his last years, the late Pope Pius XII alluded to several revivals of the problem of monogenesis. At the start of his pontificate, in the encyclical *Summi Pontificatus* (October 1939), the Holy Father deplored "the neglect of that law of human solidarity and love, dictated and imposed as much by the common origin or the uniformity of the rational nature of all men (pertaining to all people whatsoever), as by the redemptive sacrifice on the altar of the Cross, which Jesus Christ offered to His heavenly Father for sinful mankind." [24]

In a discourse delivered November 30, 1941, before the members of the Pontifical Academy, Pius XII stressed the fact that "from a man there can be born only another man, who can call him father and procrea-

[23] Denzinger, 2123.
[24] *Acta Apostolicae Sedis,* 31 (1939), 490.

tor."[25] Regarding the formation of Eve the Holy Father speaks as follows: "The helpmate given by God to man likewise stems from that man and is flesh of his flesh; she is formed as a companion, that is, on the model of the man, because she was taken from the man."[26] Is the Pope doing any more here than quoting the account from Genesis? At all events, it seems to us that this discourse could hardly furnish an authoritative argument in favor of the opinion that Eve was formed from some material element of Adam's body.

It is especially in one of his last encyclicals, *Humani Generis* (August 1950), that Pope Pius XII devoted a passage to the question of monogenesis. First he points out that a Catholic should examine with great care the scientific hypotheses which bear on the teachings of Holy Scripture and Tradition: "If such hypotheses be directly or indirectly opposed to the doctrine revealed by God, they would constitute an entirely unacceptable postulate." Therefore the Church allows us to debate the not yet definitely demonstrated biological theory concerning the origin of the human body, "on condition that the special creation of the soul by God be maintained, and that the greatest caution be observed."

"When, however, there is a question of another conjectural opinion, namely polygenism, the children of the Church by no means enjoy such liberty. For the faithful cannot embrace that opinion which maintains either that after Adam there existed on this earth true men who did

[25] Ibid., 33 (1941), 506.
[26] Ibid.

not take their origin through natural generation from him as from the first parent of all, or that Adam represents a certain number of first parents. Now it is in no way apparent how such an opinion can be reconciled with that which the sources of revealed truth and the documents of the Teaching Authority of the Church propose with regard to original sin, which proceeds from sin actually committed by an individual Adam and which through generation is passed on to all and is in everyone as his own." [27]

In this statement Pius XII obviously intends to protect the exact import of the dogmatic definition relating to original sin.[28] Original sin is not an inborn rebelliousness against supernatural love, nor a natural defect common to all men. There is no reason to speak of it as a "necessary evil" of the human creature, who, linked to matter, is nevertheless called to participate in the divine life. No, the inherited guilt dates back to a sin from the beginnings; the Council of Trent, we have seen, appeals explicitly to the transgression of Adam. The Holy Father states that, in order to protect this dogma, a believing Catholic cannot accept any form of polygenesis, not even scientific monophyletism. The reason for this is that it is not clear at all how polygenesis could be reconciled with the requirements of the faith.

Then may a Catholic henceforth argue against the doctrine of monogenesis? After the Encyclical *Humani*

[27] Encyclical *Humani Generis,* New York, Paulist Press, 1950, n. 66.
[28] Cf. the address of Pius XII to the Carmelite Fathers, in *Acta Apostolicae Sedis,* 43 (1951), 738.

Generis, it would be inconsistent with thoughtful wisdom and supernatural prudence to adopt that attitude. We should emphasize first that, even scientifically speaking, we have no conclusive proofs to exclude monogenesis. Philosophically speaking, monogenesis is perfectly admissible, if we admit that God creates when and as He wills. Finally, this tenet is evidently most apt to safeguard revealed truths.

Has the Church made a definite pronouncement on this matter? When we carefully analyze the official text of the Encyclical, it seems that the restriction of freedom on the subject of mono- or polygenesis is not necessarily irrevocable. The absence of enlightenment which results when it is in no way apparent *how* polygenesis *can* be reconciled with Revelation, is not necessarily final. It is possible (we do not say probable, nor certain) that with the passage of time the objective probability of this conciliation may become apparent, under the form, for example, of a mitigated monophyletism. In that rather questionable case, it would be beneficial to have established, as a preliminary, a clear distinction between monogenesis and the very nucleus of the doctrine of original sin.[29] In any case, it would be expedient to remember that, in all probability, bodily propagation is not an explicit element of that article of faith.

[29] After the encyclical *Humani Generis*, polygenism is no longer an opinion which may be discussed without danger to the faith. However, no reproach is attached to the research which is required for the progress of doctrine. Cf. the address of the Holy Father to the Carmelite Fathers: "as if we wanted to prevent the investigations, which the progress of doctrine demands" (*Acta Apostolicae Sedis*, 1951, 732).

Without doubt Pius XII, enlightened by the assistance of the Holy Spirit, has pronounced very serious words (although not infallible) against polygenesis. Nevertheless, no one is entitled to stigmatize it as a "deviation from Catholic truth," i.e., in the strict sense of the terms, to call it heresy. At the utmost it might be regarded as "a deviating and exaggerated" hypothesis.[30] When the Holy Father speaks of a deviating exaggeration, it cannot be a question of a final and irrevocable condemnation. An obedient son of the Church will not take it upon himself to defend this hypothesis or to propose it as probable; but he cannot identify it as a formal heresy.

[30] *Acta Apostolicae Sedis*, 43 (1951), 732: "Aberrantes et immoderatas doctrinas."

Conclusion

THIS STUDY of the origin of man, from the religious point of view of the Bible (neither scientific nor philosophical), has endeavored to eliminate a few false problems and unauthorized solutions.

We have mainly emphasized that the formal object of the Bible differs from that of scientific inquiry. Similarly, we have appealed to a sound sense of history, in virtue of which we cannot, in a particular, inspired document, look for the answer to questions which are irrelevant to the historic perspective of the author. Therefore, we have tried to establish a critical distinction between the "dogma" of the hereditary transmission of original sin, and the theological question regarding the *manner* of that transmission.

Always we have started from the conviction that the doctrine of the Holy Catholic Church cannot be *borne out by arguments* which, finally, are not doctrinal. Any revival of Concordism remains pernicious and blamable.

Apparently there is today, among Catholic exegetes, a great unanimity in affirming that the question of the age of humanity is neither asked nor resolved by the Bible. No one at present continues to defend the numerical accuracy of biblical chronology.

The second problem also, which treats of the evolution of the human body, is actually separated more and more from the ancient Genesis texts, considered in themselves. Obviously, it is always necessary to safeguard the free creative activity of God with respect to the soul, and His Providence with regard to evolutionary development.

Finally, the third problem, that of monogenesis, entered into a critical phase, after the publication of the encyclical "Humani Generis." Admitting that the Holy Father has unequivocally taken his stand, the Catholic exegete must wholly conform to his directives. Therefore, he cannot propose any exegesis tending to prove positively and arbitrarily the thesis of "theological polygenesis." Still less has he the right to spread that opinion indirectly. Besides, the polygenetic hypothesis is neither scientifically evident nor philosophically clear.

Granting, incidentally, that we are dealing with a point which has not yet been defined, it seemed expedient to us to distinguish between the doctrine of faith proposed by the Church and certain proofs or arguments which perhaps have little or nothing to do with the question which interests us. For that reason, we have submitted the text of Rom 5, and the teachings of the Council of Trent, to a minute examination, in order to define their exact meaning. Throughout, our ultimate aim was to form consciences, and to determine the attitude which the believing Catholic may adopt without failing in his duty. To solve the burning problem of monogenesis, it would be better, in our humble opinion, not to "beg" the lifeless texts; the solution can be supplied only through the living Magisterium of our Holy Mother the Church.